A
QUESTION
OF
RANGERS

The publishers would like to thank George Ashton and Sportapic for their help in the production of this book.

A
QUESTION
OF
RANGERS

Foreword by
DEREK JOHNSTONE

CollinsWillow
An Imprint of HarperCollins*Publishers*

First published in 1991 by
Collins Willow
an imprint of HarperCollins Publishers
London

© HarperCollins Publishers 1991

A CIP catalogue record for this book
is available from the British Library

ISBN 0 00218424 9

Typesetting by Michael Mepham, Frome, Somerset
Printed and bound in Great Britain by
HarperCollins Manufacturing, Glasgow

CONTENTS

FOREWORD

Here's a quiz question for you: which 16-year-old once scored a winning goal for Rangers in a national cup final?

This is one I can definitely answer because, as Max Bygraves would say, I was that soldier!

That's going back over 20 years – or for me at least four stone – and a lot has happened to the Light Blues since then. There have been many memorable moments at Ibrox and I know that supporters enjoy testing their knowledge of all the facts and feats and comings and goings.

Well, this is simply THE quiz book for all Rangers fans. There are OVER 1000 questions on the Gers. Many of them are on recent seasons so you can see how much you remember about the triumphs, the set-backs, the great goals, the big European nights etc.

There are also a few teasers on past glories and on old timers like Alan Morton, Willie Thornton and Jim Baxter. But don't worry – you don't have to be an expert to answer them all!

So if you're a 'Bluenose' and you like a bit of fun competition then why not have a go at... *A QUESTION OF RANGERS.*

DEREK JOHNSTONE

— 1 —
RANGERS
HOT SHOTS

Mark Hateley – see question 1

1. From which French club did Mark Hateley join Rangers?

2. He scored five goals for Rangers during 1988–89 and later became a broadcaster on satellite TV – who is he?

3. Who became the Premier League's leading scorer of all time when he netted for Gers against Motherwell in December 1989?

4. Rangers signed striker Bobby Williamson from which team in November 1983?

5. Who bagged five goals against Dunfermline at East End Park in 1974?

6. Which Rangers striker was voted the PFA's Young Player of the Year in 1986–87?

7. Who, along with Ally McCoist, was joint-top League scorer for 1983–84?

8. In November 1968, which striker, making his debut for Rangers, scored a hat-trick within the space of five minutes?

9. Davie Dodds joined Rangers from Aberdeen. For which Swiss club did he play before signing for the Dons?

10. Who was the striker who became the first player to have his fee set by a transfer tribunal in Scotland when he joined Gers in June 1980?

11. Who was Rangers' top scorer in League matches during 1990–91?

12. What was the collective nickname given to the 1960s striking duo of Jimmy Millar and Ralph Brand?

13. Who was the ex-Rangers striker who played in the 1988 Olympic Football Tournament?

14. What did Ally McCoist win in both 1988 and 1989 as a result of finishing leading goalscorer in the Skol Cup?

15. Who hit five goals against Stirling Albion in a 1966 League Cup tie?

16. In August 1983, Sandy Clark scored a winning goal against Celtic – in the final of which competition?

17. Who was the inside-left, signed from Airdrie in 1927, who went on to hit 281 goals for Rangers?

18. Which striker came to Ibrox from Dundee in May 1984 but was put up for transfer only 16 months later?
19. Can you name the Rangers star of the 1930s and '40s who played for the club in all five of the old forward positions?
20. Which Englishman was the leading League goalscorer in the 1988–89 season?

— 2 —
HAPPY
NEW YEAR

Rangers go 2-0 up in the 1991 Ne'erday match

1. Who scored Rangers' winner in the Parkhead Old Firm game of January 1990?

2. Can you name either of the Rangers players who made their Old Firm debut in the 2–0 Ibrox victory over Celtic in January 1987?

3. Who fired Rangers ahead in that match?

4. Who missed a penalty for Celtic in the 1985 Ne'erday encounter?

5. In the January 1988 match, Rangers went down 2–0. Which player did they lose after a clash with Celtic's Lex Baillie?

6. And who took his position?

7. Who scored the only goal of the 1976 New Year match at Ibrox?

8. In 1982, the game was again decided by a solitary goal. Who converted a penalty after 72 minutes to win the match for Rangers?

9. Why was the 1984 Ne'erday match postponed?

10. Who scored twice in the 4–1 demolition of Celtic in January 1989?

11. In January 1973, Alfie Conn sealed the Old Firm match with a 89th-minute header – for which team?

12. Can you name the two scorers who helped Rangers 'bring in' 1991 with a 2–0 triumph over their old rivals at Ibrox?

13. On January 7th, 1978, there was a highly-controversial goal in Rangers' 3–1 victory. Who scored it while most of the Celtic team were claiming a penalty at the other end of the pitch?

14. Who made his debut for Rangers in the 1988 Ne'erday game?

15. And who scored twice for Celtic that day?

16. Which midfielder, later to join Motherwell, hit Rangers' only reply in their 2–1 Ibrox defeat of January 1983?

17. After 20 minutes of the 1989 match, Celtic's Anton Rogan conceded a penalty when he upended which Rangers striker?

18. Rangers' 1990 victory at Parkhead was their first Ne'erday win there since 1964. Who scored the winner on that occasion?

19. Celtic's international goalkeeper Ally Hunter was beaten three times in the 1975 match. Can you name any of the Gers scorers?

20. In January 1969, a 60th-minute John Greig penalty separated the sides. Who was the Celtic player penalised for handball?

— 3 —
SPANIARDS
BY THE SCORE

Valencia take the lead in the 1979 Cup-Winners' Cup tie at Ibrox

1. Which Spanish team inflicted Rangers' heaviest-ever European defeat, in the 1963–64 Champions' Cup?

2. In the 1979 European Cup-Winners' Cup, who scored Rangers' goal in the 1–1 away draw with Spanish Cup holders Valencia?

3. Which Gers full-back scored an unfortunate deflected own goal in the Ibrox return leg?

4. Who headed the equaliser for Gers after 24 minutes of that game?

5. Valencia knocked out Rangers with two further goals from their Argentinian international striker. Can you name him?

6. Which team from the Northern Spanish town of Pamplona defeated Rangers in the 1985–86 UEFA Cup?

7. In the 1968–69 Fairs Cup quarter-final, Rangers beat Athletic Bilbao 4–1 in the first leg. What was the return leg score?

8. Rangers' captain in that tie missed a penalty in the first leg. Who was he?

9. Who was the Gers winger ordered off in the return match in Spain?

10. In August 1987, which Spanish side took part in the Rangers International four-club tournament at Ibrox?

11. Who was their manager at that time?

12. In the 1967 European Cup-Winners' Cup quarter-final, Rangers went through at the expense of Spaniards Real Zaragoza. What was the aggregate score?

13. How was the tie decided?

14. Who missed a penalty for Gers in the second leg?

15. Which famous Hungarian star notched a hat-trick for Real Madrid against Rangers in 1963?

16. Who was the unfortunate Gers keeper who lost six goals in Madrid?

17. Another star of that Real side later managed Valencia to their 1979 victory at Ibrox. Can you name him?

18. Which Gers defender scored the only goal of the 1985 UEFA Cup First Round first-leg tie with Atletico Osasuna?

19. Who was the West German international who played for Valencia against Rangers in the 1979–80 Cup-Winners' Cup?

20. Valencia went on to win that competition – which English club did they defeat in the final?

— 4 —
THREE IN A ROW –
1990–91

Mark Hateley opens the scoring in the crunch match against Aberdeen

1. By how many points did Rangers eventually win the 1990–91 Championship from Aberdeen?

2. Who scored the Gers' first Premier League goal of the season, against Dunfermline in August?

3. Against which team did Terry Hurlock score his first League goal for the club in September?

4. Where did Terry Butcher score an unfortunate own goal in what proved to be his last match for the club?

5. Which young striker made his Premier League debut in the 1–0 home victory over St Mirren in February?

6. During 1990–91, only one team defeated Rangers in a League match at Ibrox – who was it?

7. Who came off the bench to score twice in the 2–2 home draw with Aberdeen in December?

8. Where did Gary Stevens net his first double in seven years to help Rangers to a 4–2 victory in November?

9. Who scored the Gers' first-ever goal at St Johnstone's McDiarmid Park in February?

10. Aberdeen and Rangers clashed at Pittodrie in March. Who notched the last-minute goal for the Dons which pegged Rangers' Championship lead back to six points?

11. Which midfield star missed the Championship run-in after being injured in the Scottish Cup quarter-final defeat by Celtic?

12. Who was ordered off during the League match at Parkhead in March?

13. Against which team did Ian Durrant make his long-awaited comeback in April?

14. Who was the substitute who scored a crucial 84th minute winner against St Mirren at Love Street – in Walter Smith's first match as Rangers boss?

15. In April 1991, Rangers played Dundee United in a 'live' satellite TV match which was switched to a Wednesday evening. Who dived bravely to head the only goal of that game?

16. Where did the Gers crash 3–0 on the penultimate Saturday of the season, allowing Aberdeen to overtake them in the League table?

17. Who skippered the Rangers side in their glorious 2–0 victory over the Dons in the Championship decider at Ibrox?

18. During that match, Rangers lost two defenders through injury. Who were they?

19. Can you remember who kept goal for Aberdeen that day?
20. Only two players appeared in every competitive match for Rangers during 1990–91. Can you name either of them?

— 5 —
COMINGS AND GOINGS

Nigel Spackman – see question 17

1. Who was Graeme Souness's first signing for Rangers?

2. Which English club did Alfie Conn join in July 1974?

3. Who moved from Partick Thistle to Rangers in June 1982?

4. In August 1987, this former Rangers skipper joined Blackburn Rovers – who was he?

5. From which club was Tommy Cowan signed?

6. Striker Jim Forrest went to which English Second Division team in 1967?

7. In June 1987, Graeme Souness signed which former Liverpool team-mate from Maccabi Tel Aviv?

8. Which team did Ian McCall join in January 1990?

9. Who left Ibrox in November 1983, signing for Manchester City in a £25,000 deal?

10. Can you remember the Glentoran full-back signed by Rangers in February 1984?

11. Where did Ted McMinn go in 1987?

12. Which Rangers striker joined Philadelphia Furies in April 1978?

13. Who moved with team-mate Iain Ferguson from Dens Park to Ibrox in 1984?

14. From which club was Gordon Smith acquired in August 1977?

15. Which midfielder, who joined Rangers from East Fife in March 1987, made only six League appearances before moving on to Hearts in 1989?

16. Who arrived at Ibrox from Toronto Blizzard in October 1983 in John Greig's last signing as Rangers boss?

17. From which club did Nigel Spackman join the Gers?

18. Who was the young Rangers player who spent 1989–90 on loan to Hong Kong outfit Lai Sun?

19. Which English Midlands side did Colin Stein join in October 1972?

20. In June 1986, Graeme Souness freed five players. Can you name any three of them?

— 6 —
JUST CHAMPION! –
1989–90

Terry Butcher holds the Championship trophy aloft

1. At which ground did Rangers clinch the 1990 Premier League title?

2. Who headed the goal which won that match?

3. In which month did the Gers top the League table for the first time?

4. Can you name either of the two players who played in every game of 1989–90?

5. Against which team did Ray Wilkins make his farewell appearance in November 1989?

6. Who turned out for Rangers in central defence, midfield and at full-back?

7. Which team won at Ibrox on the opening day of the 1989–90 season?

8. In January, Rangers had a crucial 2–0 victory over Aberdeen at Ibrox – can you name either of the scorers that day?

9. Which ex-Ranger scored Motherwell's winner in the October meeting of the clubs at Fir Park?

10. How many of their ten penalty awards did Rangers convert during 1989–90?

11. Who scored Rangers' last goal of the 1980s, against St Mirren at Ibrox on 23rd December?

12. Which was the only side to beat Rangers twice in the League?

13. Where did Nigel Spackman make his debut for the Gers?

14. Who was sent off in the League match against Dundee at Ibrox in September?

15. Rangers played which English team for the Zenith Cup in December?

16. Which midfielder made a surprise return to the first team against Dundee United in April?

17. In December, Rangers drew 1–1 with Dundee United in a match played during a torrential rainstorm. Who scored the Gers' equaliser that day?

18. Which full-back's goal secured both points from the trip to Dunfermline in January?

19. Between February 3rd and March 17th, the Ibrox men drew four consecutive League matches. Can you name any of the teams with which they shared the points?

20. Who scored his first goal of the season in the last game, against Hearts at Tynecastle in May?

— 7 —
THE
YELLOW JERSEY

Chris Woods

1. Chris Woods and Bonny Ginzburg both made their Premier League debuts for Rangers at the same ground – which one?

2. From which Second Division club did Rangers sign Lindsay Hamilton in 1986?

3. Which British goalkeeping record did Chris Woods set during the 1986-87 season?

4. Bonny Ginzburg is an international for which country?

5. Who kept goal for Rangers in the 1967 European Cup-Winners' Cup Final?

6. By what christian name was famous Gers keeper James Dawson better known?

7. Which goalkeeper was the last line of Rangers' 'Iron Curtain' defence of the late '40s and early '50s?

8. Who was the keeper whom Rangers signed from Middlesbrough in March 1981?

9. With which club did Andy Goram win his first Scotland cap in October 1985?

10. Which Gers goalkeeper had to drop out of a 1975 European Cup tie with St Etienne after being injured in the pre-match warm-up?

11. Who was the Danish international goalkeeper whom Rangers signed from Morton in July 1967?

12. Who kept goal for Rangers in the 1987 Skol Cup Final?

13. During Rangers successful 1974–75 Scottish League Championship campaign, who played in goal in all 34 matches?

14. What nationality was Gerry Neef, Rangers keeper of the early '70s?

15. Who kept goal for the 1964 'Treble' side?

16. Apart from football, at which other sport has Andy Goram been capped by Scotland?

17. Lindsay Hamilton played on loan for which club in the 1988–89 Second Division?

18. Why did Chris Woods miss the 1987 Skol Cup Final?

19. Who played in goal for Rangers in the Scottish Cup Finals of 1981 and 1982?

20. Goalkeepers Peter McCloy and Nicky Walker both joined Rangers from which club?

— 8 —
IN THE
BEGINNING

The Rangers line-up back in 1876-77

1. In which year were Rangers founded – 1872, 1882 or 1892?
2. Where in Glasgow was Flesher's Haugh, where Rangers played their first matches?
3. What was the surname of brothers Peter and Moses who were among the four original founders of Rangers?
4. Who were Scotland's top club during the early years of Rangers' history?

5. In 1886–87, Rangers reached the semi-finals of which cup competition?

6. Where did Rangers play immediately before moving to Ibrox in 1887?

7. In the first Ibrox Stadium's official opening match of August 1887, Rangers lost 8–1 to a Lancashire team who were soon to become the first champions of the English League. Can you name the team?

8. With which current Second Division club did Rangers share the first-ever Scottish League Championship?

9. Who won the first-ever Old Firm game, in front of only 2,000 fans in May 1888?

10. Rangers' Championship team of 1898–99 won how many of their eighteen League matches?

11. Why was the Scottish Cup witheld after the Rangers-Celtic Final of 1909?

12. Who was the inside-forward, signed from Kilmarnock in 1915, who went on to win seven League Championship medals with Rangers?

13. How many times did the Gers win the League during the 1920s?

14. Rangers' first team lifted four trophies in the 1929–30 season. The Scottish League and Cup were two – can you name either of the other two?

15. Who was the Celtic goalkeeper tragically killed after an accidental clash with Rangers forward Sam English during an Old Firm League match in 1931?

16. Which leading English side, managed by Herbert Chapman, did Rangers defeat over two games during 1933–34, in an unofficial 'British Championship' decider?

17. In 1936, Gers beat which now-defunct team to win their third successive Scottish Cup?

18. Where did Rangers play a ten-match tour during the summer of 1928?

19. Which young Rangers star scored the only goal of the match, on his debut against Arsenal in 1938?

20. In 1928, the Ibrox men scored a famous Scottish Cup Final victory over Celtic. What was the score?

— 9 —
AUF WIEDERSEHEN

Rangers meet Bayern once again in 1989

1. Which West German club knocked Rangers out of Europe on three occasions between 1979 and 1988?

2. Who scored Rangers' goal in their 1–1 draw with Borussia Moenchengladbach in the 1986 UEFA Cup match at Ibrox?

3. How many games have Rangers played against Bayern Munich in European competition?

4. Where did Bayern beat Rangers in the 1967 European Cup-Winners' Cup Final?

5. Can you name the Bundesliga team from Dusseldorf which the Ibrox men defeated in the 1979–80 Cup-Winners' Cup?

6. Henning Jensen scored twice for Borussia Moenchengladbach in a 1973 European tie at Ibrox. What nationality is he?

7. Which notorious German goalkeeper played at Ibrox for Cologne in 1979 and 1982 matches?

8. In the 1970 Rangers-Bayern Munich Fairs Cup clash at Ibrox, Gerd Muller netted for the Germans but which striker scored Rangers' equaliser?

9. Which German side did Rangers eliminate from Europe in both 1966 and 1982?

10. Who scored Bayern's winner in the 1967 Cup-Winners' Cup Final?

11. Rangers defeated Cologne 2–1 at Ibrox in the first leg of their 1982 UEFA Cup tie. What was the result of the return match?

12. Who scored Rangers' only goal in their 3–1 Ibrox defeat by Bayern in the 1989–90 European Cup?

13. Can you name the Bayern captain who scored their third goal in that match with a screaming shot?

14. Which Scotsman lined up against Rangers that night?

15. Who was the West German international striker who scored in both legs of Cologne's 1979 European Cup victory over the Gers?

16. Which German team defeated Rangers on their way to the 1960 European Cup Final where they crashed 7–3 to Real Madrid?

17. Who hit two goals for Moenchengladbach against Rangers in 1973 and later bossed Bayern to victory over the Ibrox men?

18. Which international winger played for Cologne in all three of their European meetings with the Gers between 1979 and 1988?

19. Rangers' second goal against Fortuna Dusseldorf in the 1979 Cup-Winners' Cup match at Ibrox was a header from the smallest player on the park. Who was this?

20. Which now-departed striker headed Gers' goal in the 1–1 Ibrox draw with Cologne in the 1988–89 UEFA Cup?

— 10 —
SUPER ALLY

Ally in action

1. In which year did Ally McCoist eventually join Rangers?

2. Which English club did he leave to come to Ibrox?

3. What Rangers record did Ally break in the match against Celtic in April 1990?

4. Who previously held that record?

5. Which was Ally's first senior club?

6. And which Lanarkshire club wanted to sign him as a school-boy?

7. Against which country did he make his Scotland debut in 1986?

8. Which manager signed Ally for Rangers?

9. What was the first medal won by him in a Light Blue jersey?

10. In September 1987, he notched a double for Scotland – against which team?

11. What TV award did Ally receive in 1987?

12. Against which club did he score his first hat-trick for the Gers?

13. In March 1988, Ally played a solo striking role in a European Cup match in Bucharest – what was remarkable about his appearance in the team for that game?

14. His first European goal for Rangers came against which Irish side in 1984?

15. In which competition did Ally score a hat-trick against Celtic in 1986?

16. One of Ally's fellow strikers at Sunderland later played with him at Ibrox. Who was this?

17. Who was his first Rangers striking partner?

18. In November 1989, Ally notched a crucial World Cup goal at Hampden – against which country?

19. Who was the manager who signed him for Sunderland?

20. Did Ally travel to Mexico with the 1986 World Cup squad?

— 11 —
UP FOR THE CUP

Another full house for an Old Firm Cup Final

1. How many times did Rangers win the Scottish Cup during the 1980s?

2. In the 1981 Scottish Cup Final, who missed a penalty for Rangers in the last minute of normal time?

3. Who was the Dundee United goalkeeper who saved it?

4. Rangers and Hibs played three games to decide the 1979 Scottish Cup. What was the score of the first two?

5. Who scored twice for the Gers in the third game?

6. Which Rangers defender notched the winner in the 1973 Old Firm Cup Final, from all of six inches?

7. Celtic had earlier tied that match at 2–2 with a penalty. Who conceded it when he 'saved' from Parkhead striker Dixie Deans?

8. Which forward hit two goals in the 3–1 Cup Final win over Dundee in 1964?

9. Which player in the Dundee team that day later joined up at Ibrox?

10. In 1981, who was left out of the first Cup Final match against Dundee United but came in to score one Rangers' goal and make two others in the 4–1 replay victory?

11. Another player, who was only a substitute in the first game, scored twice for Gers that night. Who was that?

12. Who was Hibs' international star whose unfortunate own goal won the 1979 Scottish Cup for Rangers?

13. Which fellow Glasgow club had Gers beaten in the semi-finals that year?

14. Who sat on the ball during Rangers' 1963 Scottish Cup Final replay win over Celtic?

15. Who scored Dundee United's goal in the 1981 Final replay?

16. Which team did Rangers defeat in the semi-final at Parkhead that season?

17. To the nearest ten seconds, what was the time of Derek Johnstone's opener in the 1976 Cup Final win over Hearts?

18. In which year did Danish full-back Kai Johansen score a famous Scottish Cup winning goal against Celtic?

19. Goals from Brand and Wilson gave Rangers a 2–0 Final victory over which team in 1962?

20. Who captained the victorious Rangers side of 1981?

— 12 —
DARK BLUE RANGERS

Richard Gough in his country's colours

1. Which famous Ranger won 53 Scotland caps between 1947 and 1957?

2. Who won his first international honour in Scotland's 'B' match against Yugoslavia in March 1990?

3. In December 1988, which two Rangers played for Scotland in a friendly against Italy in Perugia?

4. Who was the last Rangers player to score for Scotland against England at Wembley?

5. Can you name the Ibrox full-back partners who appeared together four times for Scotland during the 1960s?

6. Two Gers were capped during the 1982–83 season. Jim Bett was one – who was the other?

7. Which young midfielder made his international debut against Hungary in September 1987?

8. Who was the Rangers left-back who was famed for his ability to keep England's Stanley Matthews at bay?

9. Which Ibrox midfield man won his only cap against Switzerland in 1976?

10. Derek Ferguson made his first Scotland appearance in Malta in March 1988 – can you remember the score of that game?

11. In October 1961, Rangers players hit all of Scotland's goals in their 6–1 victory over Northern Ireland. Name any of the scorers that day.

12. Who, in 1975, was the last Rangers goalkeeper to play for Scotland?

13. Can you name the famous Ibrox half-back line which was temporarily re-united in Scotland's sensational 3–2 victory over World Champions England in 1967?

14. Who was the last Ranger to play in a winning Scotland team at Wembley?

15. Ally McCoist scored for Scotland in a 1990 World Cup warm-up match at Pittodrie – who were the opposition?

16. Which Ranger scored in all three Home International matches of May 1969?

17. Who broke his leg against England at Wembley in 1963?
18. And who was the Ibrox team-mate who filled his position in that game?
19. Derek Johnstone scored two goals in his fourteen international matches. Can you name either of the countries against which he netted?
20. Which Ranger was Scotland's skipper in their 5–1 thrashing by England in 1975?

— 13 —
HAT-TRICK
HEROES

Colin Stein – see question 15

1. Who hit a European hat-trick for Rangers against Finnish side Ilves Tampere in September 1986?

2. Who was the first Ranger to notch three goals in one match during 1990–91?

3. Which team were defeated 6–2 that night?

4. Who scored a hat-trick for Gers in a rare 6–1 drubbing of Aberdeen in 1977?

5. Dundee beat Rangers 3–2 in November 1985 – who scored all three goals for the Dens Parkers?

6. Who is the only Rangers player ever to score a hat-trick in an away European fixture?

7. Which striker scored a treble against Clyde in March 1969 and was then ordered off for retaliation?

8. During the 1987–88 season, Ally McCoist notched two hat-tricks within three weeks against the same Premier team – which one?

9. Which Aberdeen midfielder struck three times in the Dons' 5–1 defeat of Rangers in the 1976 League Cup semi-final?

10. Which striker, later to become a famous manager, scored a hat-trick in Rangers' 10–2 win over Raith Rovers in 1967?

11. How many hat-tricks did Robert Fleck hit in the 1986–87 season?

12. Against which team did he score two of these?

13. Who scored a Scottish Cup semi-final hat-trick against Aberdeen in 1969?

14. In March 1955, winger Alex Scott scored a hat-trick on his Rangers debut against his home-town club – who was this?

15. Can you name the sides on the receiving end of Colin Stein hat-tricks in the striker's first two games for Gers?

16. In Rangers' 7–0 win over Morton of September 1987, Ally McCoist and which other player each netted three goals?

17. Who was the first Ranger to notch a hat-trick in a European match?

18. Who scored three times for Motherwell against the Gers in January 1983?

19. Which young Rangers striker scored a treble in the home leg of the 1983 European Cup-Winners' Cup tie with Valletta of Malta?

20. On New Year's Day 1955, which winger wrote himself into the history books with a hat-trick against Celtic?

— 14 —
DUNDEE,
HAMILTON...

Robert Prytz in action at Dundee

1. In the 1980–81 Premier League, Rangers won 8–1 away to which team?

2. Which current First Division team did they visit in the 1970 Scottish Cup, winning 7–0?

3. Where did Meadowbank play Rangers in the second leg of the 1984 Skol Cup semi-final?

4. In which year did the Gers first notch a Premier League victory at Pittodrie?

5. And who scored the winning goal that day?

6. Where did Rangers clinch the 1975 Scottish League Championship?

7. Who scored four goals at Kilmarnock in a 1982 League Cup tie?

8. In the 1963–64 Championship season, Rangers lost only one away League fixture. Which team beat them?

9. In February 1987, the Ibrox men inflicted which team's first home defeat in 18 months when they beat them 5–2?

10. Which Premier side were defeated 5–0 away in the 1981 Scottish Cup?

11. Where have Rangers beaten both Stenhousemuir and Stirling Albion in Skol Cup ties of recent seasons?

12. Who was the Kilmarnock goalkeeper who lost six goals to Rangers at Rugby Park in September 1974?

13. In 1982, Rangers played Aberdeen at Pittodrie a week before the teams met in the Scottish Cup Final. What was the result of that League game?

14. On a visit to which other Glasgow club did Jim Forrest score four times in September 1963?

15. Against which team did Rangers hit five goals in both their away Premier League fixtures of 1977–78?

16. Where was the 1987 League Title clinched?

17. Which Inverness side did Rangers defeat 6–0 away in the 1984 Scottish Cup?

18. Where did the Gers record their highest competitive away victory of the 1990–91 season?

19. Who netted a hat-trick in the 8–1 win at Kilmarnock in 1980?

20. What is Rangers' highest Premier League victory at Dundee?

— 15 —
JUST WILLIAM

Who is this? – see question 5

1. Which Rangers star, of over 700 appearances, was never known at Ibrox by his real name – William?

2. Who was the short-sighted, 5′ 4″ right-winger of the successful 1960s Gers team?

3. Which English team did Ibrox favourite Willie Johnston join in 1972?

4. 1950s' star forward Billy Simpson was an international for which country?

5. Which 'Willie' was left-back in Rangers' victorious European Cup-Winners' Cup team?

6. Who made 21 appearances for Rangers between 1981 and 1986 when he left to join I. F. Elfsborg of Sweden?

7. In 1978, which 'Billy' was John Greig's first signing for Rangers?

8. Who was, either alone or jointly, Rangers' leading League goalscorer in the first six post-war seasons?

9. And who was the forward, signed from Albion Rovers, who was leading scorer in all competitions in 1950 and 1951?

10. Winger Billy Mackay quit Rangers because of injury. Which national side did Rangers play in a testimonial for him?

11. He later made a comeback – with which Premier side?

12. In July 1969, Willie Henderson played against Wales at Cardiff – for which team?

13. Which English club did Henderson join in 1972?

14. From which Lothian club did Willie Woodburn sign for Rangers?

15. Which 'Willie' was top overall scorer in 1953–54?

16. Which other Glasgow team did goalkeeper Billy Ritchie join in 1968?

17. In September 1988, Billy Davies scored a cracking goal at Ibrox – for which club?

18. Who won the more caps – Willie Henderson or Willie Johnston?

19. For which club did Willie Johnston last play in the Premier League?

20. How many players with the christian name 'William' were in the squad that won Rangers' first 'Treble' in 1948–49?

— 16 —
BLUE
IS THE COLOUR

Mo and Mark get kitted out

1. Which sportswear company supplies Rangers' 1991–92 kit?

2. In which year did the name of *McEwans* first appear on the Rangers jersey?

3. What colour was the alternative strip used from 1978 to 1982?

4. The 1967–68 season saw a big change from the traditional Rangers style. What distinctive feature was missing from the new jersey?

5. And what was added to the jersey for the first time this century?

6. What was the unfamiliar strip worn by Rangers in their 1978 European Cup victory over Juventus?

7. Can you describe the design of the 'away' strip used in 1988–89 and 1989–90?

8. That strip was similar in style to which European team's kit?

9. Rangers first wore it in a testimonial match for which player?

10. What colours did Rangers wear in their first Scottish Cup Final appearance?

11. Which company supplied Rangers playing kit prior to 1990?

12. What was the new feature of the jersey introduced in 1982–83?

13. What colour of socks did the 'Treble' winning sides of the 1960s and '70s wear?

14. What was Rangers' strip in their 1964 Scottish Cup Final victory over Dundee?

15. Can you describe the style of collar worn from 1978 to 1982?

16. In which year did the Rangers jersey first carry a sponsor's name?

17. Who were the first shirt sponsors?

18. What colour of socks did the Championship team of 1986–87 play in?

19. What was the strip worn by Rangers between 1879 and 1883?

20. Who threw his No.8 jersey to fans in Tannadice Street after the Gers' 1990 Championship triumph?

— 17 —
THE MIDFIELD MEN

Ian Durrant – see questions 3 and 17

1. What number did Ray Wilkins wear during his time at Ibrox?

2. Which midfielder was signed from Aston Villa in October 1988?

3. Against which team did Ian Durrant score his first goal for Rangers?

4. Which Ibrox midfielder of the 1980s was signed as a striker for a Scottish record fee in February 1980?

5. Who was the former Hibs midfield man who played in the 1976 'Treble' winning team?

6. From which club did Rangers sign Ian McMillan for £10,000 in October 1958?

7. Which midfielder made his Ibrox debut as a 15-year-old in Tom Forsyth's 1982 testimonial match against Swansea?

8. What was John Brown's first club?

9. In which year did Alex MacDonald leave Ibrox to join Hearts?

10. How many goals did Ray Wilkins score for Rangers?

11. For which midfielder did Rangers pay £30,000 to Montrose in August 1975?

12. Who was the powerful inside-forward, signed from Preston in 1955, who helped Rangers win two League Championships before moving to Hibs in 1960?

13. Diminutive midfield star of the 1980s, Robert Prytz, was an international for which country?

14. Ian Ferguson scored the winning goal in the 1987 Scottish Cup Final – for which team was he then playing?

15. From which junior club was Bobby Russell acquired in 1977?

16. Who was the former Rangers midfielder who scored an own goal while playing for Raith Rovers in a 1989 Scottish Cup tie at Ibrox?

17. In which year did Ian Durrant make his Premier League debut?

18. Rangers signed Ray Wilkins from which club in November 1987?

19. Which midfield man was signed from Queen's Park in 1945 and went on to win six League and five Scottish Cup medals before his retirement in 1961?

20. Derek Ferguson was loaned to which Premier League club during 1989–90?

— 18 —
EARLY BATHS

Rangers tussle with Hearts – see questions 12 and 13

1. In September 1985, two Rangers players were ordered off against Aberdeen at Ibrox. Can you name them?

2. Who was the centre-half, given a life ban by the SFA in 1954, after he had been ordered off for the fifth time?

3. Which Turkish club had two players sent off during a 1973 European Cup-Winners' Cup match at Ibrox?

4. In a January 1987 match against Hamilton at Ibrox, Rangers were reduced to nine men after the expulsion of which two players?

5. What was unusual about John McClelland's ordering off at Dundee in May 1983?

6. In December 1989, Mark Walters was ordered off at a Premier League ground where he had also been dismissed exactly one year earlier – where was that?

7. Who was sent off in Rangers' first-ever Premier League match?

8. Can you name the three players who were ordered off in the infamous Rangers-Celtic match of October 1987?

9. Which Ranger received his marching orders in the 1959–60 European Cup tie against Red Star in Bratislava?

10. In the Aberdeen-Rangers match of February 1986, two players were sent off – can you name them?

11. Who was the Dunfermline player ordered off in their 3–0 Ibrox defeat of April 1974?

12. Three players were sent off after a rumpus in the Rangers-Hearts game of August 1985. Who was the Rangers man involved?

13. One of the Hearts players also dismissed in that match was a former Ibrox star – who was he?

14. In the 1968–69 Fairs Cup, John Greig was ordered off in an away tie against a Yugoslavian team from Novi Sad – can you name them?

15. Where was Ian Ferguson sent off in March 1991?

16. Who was captaining Rangers in his last match before returning to Canadian soccer when he was ordered off against Celtic in April 1984?

17. Which Ranger had three early baths during the 1980–81 season?

18. Which striker was sent off in Rangers 2–0 defeat at Aberdeen in January 1983?

19. Tommy McLean was ordered off in a 1981 European Cup-Winners' Cup match in Eastern Europe – can you remember Gers' opponents?

20. Who was the Hibs player sent off at Ibrox in April 1991?

— 19 —
FINAL FLINGS

It's 'no goal' and Rangers see their hopes fade in the 1989 Cup Final

1. Which Ranger had a late 'equaliser' disallowed in the 1989 Scottish Cup Final?

2. Who headed Aberdeen's extra-time winner in the 1983 Final against Rangers?

3. How many times have Rangers lost in a replay of a Scottish Cup Final?

4. Which defender did Gers lose through concussion, just before half-time of the 1982 Final with Aberdeen?

5. That match finished 1–1 after 90 minutes – what was the final score?

6. Which of Aberdeen's scorers that day later played for Rangers?

7. Can you remember who headed Rangers' solitary goal?

8. Which Ibrox full-back broke his jaw in the 1971 Cup Final against Celtic?

9. Who took his place in the replay?

10. In that 1971 Final, the Rangers No.12 became the first substitute ever to score in a Scottish Cup Final – who was he?

11. Who deflected a Danny McGrain shot past Peter McCloy for the only goal of the 1980 Final?

12. Which ex-Ranger was in the Celtic team which defeated Gers 1–0 in 1977?

13. Who scored the winner in that game, with a controversial penalty?

14. Can you remember who was adjudged to have handled the ball on the goal-line?

15. Which two internationalists were on the bench for Rangers in 1989?

16. Who slipped home Celtic's winner in that match?

17. In which year did a 100,000-plus crowd last watch Rangers in a Scottish Cup Final?

18. Which striker played his last game for Rangers in the 1969 Cup Final defeat by Celtic?

19. Who was the Rangers star missing that day because of suspension?

20. Can you remember which Celt put through his own goal in the 1971 Final replay?

— 20 —
SLIM JIM

Jim Baxter during his second spell at Ibrox

1. Which was Jim Baxter's first senior club?

2. In which year did he sign for Rangers?

3. How much did they pay for him – £750, £7,500 or £17,500?

4. As well as Rangers and Scotland, for which other team did Jim play during 1961–62?

5. In which year did he score both of Scotland's goals in their 2–1 victory over England at Wembley?

6. In 18 appearances against Celtic between 1960 and 1965, how many times was Jim on the losing side?

7. What number did he like to wear for Rangers?

8. During a vital World Cup play-off match of 1961, Jim got into a heated argument with a team-mate over the trainer's sponge. Who was the Celtic player involved?

9. In 1967, Baxter inspired his country to a famous Wembley triumph over World Champions England. Who netted Scotland's winner that day?

10. Which English club signed Jim in May 1965?

11. And which other First Division club paid £100,000 for him in December 1967?

12. With which famous West Indian cricketer did Jim strike up a friendship during his time in England?

13. Which Rangers manager brought Baxter back to Ibrox in 1969?

14. He scored his last European goal for the Gers against which Polish side?

15. In which city did Jim break his leg during a 1964 European Cup match?

16. How many Scotland caps did he win altogether – 34, 44 or 54?

17. In October 1963, Jim turned out for the 'Rest of the World' against England at Wembley. Which fellow Scot also played that night?

18. He played in five Scotland-England matches altogether – how many of these did Scotland win?

19. With which regiment did Jim complete his National Service during his first spell at Ibrox?

20. In April 1965, Jim and Willie Henderson played in a testimonial match for which famous Englishman?

— 21 —
GOING DUTCH

Rangers face the mighty Ajax in 1973

1. Which Dutch team did Rangers sensationally defeat in the 1978–79 European Cup?

2. Rangers' first Dutch opponents were a team from Rotterdam. What was their name?

3. European champions Ajax Amsterdam played Rangers as part of the 1973 centenary celebrations. What trophy was put up for the winners of the two-legged tie?

4. Which other Amsterdam side did the Gers defeat in the 1968–69 Fairs Cup?

5. In 1977, Rangers lost to Dutch side FC Twente. From which town do they come?

6. That tie against FC Twente was in which competition?

7. Who was the superstar captain of the Ajax team which played at Ibrox in 1973?

8. Which Rangers midfielder scored in both matches against Ajax?

9. Name the twin brothers, both Dutch internationals, who played for PSV against Rangers in 1978?

10. Who scored Rangers' winning goal in the Eindhoven second leg of that 1978 tie?

11. For which other Dutch side did former Ajax star Johan Cruyff play at Ibrox in a 1984 challenge match?

12. The DWS Amsterdam goalkeeper who played against Rangers in 1968 went on to appear for Holland in two World Cup Finals. Can you name him?

13. Which Dutch team took part in the four-club Rangers International tournament in August 1987?

14. At which London ground did Rangers defeat Sparta Rotterdam in a 1960 European Cup play-off match?

15. What name was given to the playing style of the great Ajax team of the 1970s?

16. Arie Haan, who scored in both 1973 matches against Rangers, managed which German club to the 1989 UEFA Cup Final?

17. Which famous Dutch international scored a cracking first goal for Feyenoord in the 1984 challenge match at Ibrox?

18. Who was the veteran Irish striker who played for Ajax in the Rangers International tournament of 1987?

19. Which member of the FC Twente side which defeated Rangers in 1977 later became England's Footballer of the Year?

20. Ally McCoist made his Scotland debut in which Dutch town?

— 22 —
THEY SHALL NOT PASS

Richard Gough gives his thoughts

1. Where was star stopper Richard Gough born?

2. Who was the Hibs centre-half signed by Rangers for a record fee of £225,000 in July 1982?

3. Who were the full-backs in the unsuccessful European Cup-Winners' Cup Final team of 1967?

4. In which year did Gary Stevens join the Gers?

5. Which accomplished sweeper was voted Scottish Footballer of the Year in 1972?

6. Which two players shared the right-back berth in the 1987–88 season?

7. Who was the cultured defender who made over 400 appearances for Rangers between 1929 and 1941 when he stopped playing to become a director of the club?

8. From which English Fourth Division team was John McClelland signed in 1981?

9. Who took over the Rangers captaincy in the 1987–88 season, after Terry Butcher's leg break?

10. Which Rangers and Scotland defender did Tommy Docherty once call a 'carthorse' in comparison to his 'thoroughbred' Martin Buchan?

11. Who skippered the 1964 'Treble' side?

12. Who moved, along with Dave McPherson, to Hearts in 1987?

13. Which veteran centre-half played his last match for Rangers at the age of 35, in the 1982 Scottish Cup Final against Aberdeen?

14. Which current Ibrox defender played for the Football League against the Rest of the World at Wembley in August 1987?

15. From which club did both Gregor Stevens and Tom Forsyth join Rangers?

16. In 1980, who fractured his skull during Rangers' Canadian tour?

17. Stuart Munro arrived at Ibrox in 1984 – from which club did he come?

18. Who scored 93 goals for Rangers between 1965 and 1982, despite playing mainly as a full-back?

19. Known as 'Tiger', this loyal servant played over 500 games for Rangers – can you name him?

20. With which team did Richard Gough win a Premier League Championship medal in 1983?

— 23 —
WHO'S THE FELLOW
IN THE BLACK?

'Oh, come on ref!'

1. Who was the referee who disallowed a late Rangers 'equaliser' from Terry Butcher in the 1989 Scottish Cup Final?

2. Which referee was in charge of the notorious Old Firm game of October 1987 in which three players were ordered off?

3. Who was the ref who sent off Mo Johnston in the 1986 Skol Cup Final?

4. Can you name the famous English World Cup referee, who officiated in Rangers' first-ever European Cup match at Ibrox in 1956?

5. What mistake did he make in that game?

6. He later became an official in which TV game show?

7. In August 1986, which referee cut short the Premier League debut of Graeme Souness, after 37 minutes of the match against Hibs at Easter Road?

8. What nationality was Mr Ortiz de Mendibil who refereed the 1972 European Cup-Winners' Cup Final in Barcelona?

9. Who was the referee when Rangers clinched the 1987 League Championship at Pittodrie?

10. Which Aberdeen player did he appear to book twice in that game?

11. Who was the Belgian who ordered off Davie Cooper and Stuart Munro in the 1986 UEFA Cup match in Moenchengladbach?

12. Which Glasgow official retired after refereeing the 1981 Scottish Cup Final replay against Dundee United?

13. Who gave Celtic a disputed penalty for handball in the 1977 Cup Final?

14. Which referee was suspended by the SFA after allegedly being 'too lenient' with Aberdeen's Willie Miller during a 1988 match at Ibrox?

15. Who was in charge of the 1988 and 1989 Skol Cup Finals?

16. Can you remember the famous Clarkston-based referee who officiated in 23 Old Firm matches – the last being the 1971 Scottish Cup Final replay?

17. What was his rather-sarcastic nickname?

18. Who was the referee who ordered off three Rangers players in the stormy 1991 Scottish Cup quarter-final match at Parkhead?

19. Which ref awarded Rangers two penalties in the 1984 Skol Final against Celtic?

20. Who was the official in charge of the 1991 Premier League showdown match against Aberdeen at Ibrox?

— 24 —
1970s
TREBLE CHANCES

More 'Treble' joy in the 1978 Scottish Cup Final – see questions 18-20

1. Which team did Rangers defeat in the 1976 Scottish Cup Final to complete the 'Treble'?

2. Where was the Premier League title clinched that year?

3. Who headed the only goal of the League Cup Final against Celtic in October 1975?

4. Which First Division side led Rangers by 1–0 at half-time in the League Cup semi-final before eventually losing 5–1?

5. Which defender notched a hat-trick against Airdrie in a first-round section match?

6. Which team did Rangers beat in their first-ever Premier League match in August 1975?

7. Who was the leading Gers goalscorer in 1975–76?

8. Which fellow striker was second top with 13 goals?

9. In the Scottish Cup semi-final, the Ibrox men triumphed 3–2 after being 2–0 down to which team?

10. Can you remember who played in every game for Rangers that season?

11. Which team were runners-up to Rangers in both the League and Scottish Cup in the 1977–78 season?

12. Who was their manager at that time?

13. Who scored his first-ever Old Firm goal with a cracking drive in the 1978 League Cup Final?

14. That match went to extra-time – who headed Gers winner after 117 minutes?

15. Rangers had a sensational Ibrox result against Aberdeen in the third round of the League Cup – what was the score?

16. Which Second Division club were 2–1 up on the Gers with only seven minutes of the League Cup semi-final remaining?

17. Against which team was the 1977–78 League Championship clinched at Ibrox on 29th April?

18. Who was voted Man of the Match in the Scottish Cup Final against Aberdeen?

19. He crossed for which fellow midfielder to head the opening goal after 34 minutes of play?

20. Rangers went 2–0 up with another header – who scored that one?

— 25 —
THE ENGLISH
CONNECTION

Gary and Nigel enjoying the Scottish weather

1. How many Englishmen were in the Rangers side which clinched the Premier League Championship against Hearts in April 1989?

2. From which club was Graham Roberts signed?

3. Star midfielder Trevor Steven was born in which Northumberland town?

4. What was his first English League club?

5. Who were the former Sheffield Wednesday team-mates who opposed each other in the 1989 Scottish Cup Final?

6. Which Englishman joined Rangers from Doncaster Rovers in December 1986?

7. Three players who appeared in the 1984 FA Cup Final eventually became team-mates at Ibrox – can you name them?

8. Mark Walters was signed from which club?

9. Which member of Chelsea's 1984 Second Division Championship team joined Rangers in 1989?

10. Kevin Drinkell was leading goalscorer in which English Division in the 1985–86 season?

11. Which club was he with at that time?

12. In which year did both Gary Stevens and Trevor Steven make their England debut?

13. They also won a European medal with Everton that same year – in which tournament?

14. Who joined Rangers from Bolton in March 1987 and moved back south to sign for Oxford in August 1988?

15. Strikers Colin West and Mark Falco both joined the Gers from which English outfit?

16. Which Englishman made his debut for Rangers against Hearts in November 1987?

17. Chris Woods played only one match in England's disastrous 1988 European Championships campaign. Can you remember which country he faced?

18. From which Italian Second Division club was Trevor Francis signed in 1987?

19. Trevor Steven fired home his first Ibrox goal in a friendly against which leading English team?

20. Chris Vinnicombe arrived at Ibrox in November 1989. The club which he left went on to win the 1989–90 Fourth Division title – can you name them?

— 26 —
TOP SKOLARS

Mark Walters equalises for the Gers in the 1990 Final

1. Who hit Rangers' extra-time winner in the 1990 Skol Cup Final triumph over Celtic?

2. By 1989, on how many consecutive occasions had Rangers met Aberdeen in the Skol Cup Final?

3. Who scored Rangers' goal from the penalty spot in the 1989 Final against the Dons?

4. Which Premier League team did Rangers trounce 5–0 in the 1989 semi-final?

5. In the 1986 Old Firm Final, who fired Rangers ahead after 62 minutes?

6. And who equalised for Celtic eight minutes later?

7. Who captained Rangers in the 1987 Final against Aberdeen?

8. In that game, what was the score at the end of 90 minutes?

9. Can you name any of the Gers scorers?

10. Who had put Aberdeen ahead with a penalty early in the match?

11. Which midfielder missed for the Dons in the penalty shoot-out?

12. And who hit the vital kick which kept the Skol Cup at Ibrox?

13. Can you remember whose goal won the 1984–85 Skol Cup Final against Dundee United?

14. Which defender lifted the trophy that day?

15. Who scored twice in the victory over Aberdeen in 1988?

16. Can you remember who played alongside Terry Butcher in the 1986 Final against Celtic?

17. Which team had Rangers beaten in the semi-finals that year?

18. In which year did the Gers first win the Skol Cup trophy?

19. Can you name either of the two Rangers who played in all three Finals against Aberdeen between 1987 and 1989?

20. Which team defeated the Ibrox men over two legs in the semi-finals of the 1985–86 tournament?

— 27 —
BLUE MOVES

Pieter Huistra – see questions 1 and 2

1. From which club did Rangers sign Dutch international Pieter Huistra?

2. Where did Huistra score his first League goal for the club in September 1990?

3. What was Graeme Souness's last match in charge of Rangers?

4. Who was his last signing at Ibrox?

5. Which team did Derek Ferguson join in July 1990?

6. Star signing Oleg Kuznetsov appeared in only two matches at Ibrox during the 1990–91 season. Against which teams did he play?

7. From which club was Terry Butcher signed in 1986?

8. After leaving Rangers, Terry became player-manager of which English First Division side?

9. Which club did Archie Knox leave to take the assistant-manager's job at Ibrox?

10. Which Rangers player did Knox once sign for Dundee?

11. From which Scottish First Division outfit did the Gers acquire young defender Brian Reid?

12. Reid was very unlucky to be sent off in only his second Ibrox appearance. Who were the opposition that day?

13. Who was the Rangers reserve player who joined Kilmarnock in February 1991?

14. From which London club did the Gers sign Terry Hurlock in August 1990?

15. Which English Rangers star was at the centre of a controversial call-up to the Scotland squad in January 1991?

16. Can you name the Kirkintilloch ground where Rangers played several reserve fixtures during 1990–91?

17. Which Ranger captained the Scottish League side in the League Centenary match against Scotland in August 1990?

18. Against which team did Graeme Souness play his last Premier League game in April 1990?

19. Which of Rangers' Englishmen captained his country's Under-21 team during 1990–91?

20. Why did Rangers not sign the 'trialist' who scored with a superb 20-yard drive during Rangers' pre-season friendly at Dundee in August 1990?

— 28 —
GERS ON SONG

'We are Rangers – super Rangers..'

1. Which two Spanish teams are mentioned in the song 'Who's That Team'?

2. According to 'When I Was Walking Down The Copland Road', who did the singer meet there?

3. Which 'Queen' song did Rangers fans adopt as a celebratory anthem in the 1970s?

4. Which young midfield star is 'Blue and White Dynamite' according to Ibrox supporters?

5. Sandy Jardine teamed up with which Scotland team-mate to make a record called 'Each Saturday'?

6. What was the title of Bill Barclay's tribute to the Gers?

7. 'There's only one Gary Stevens' is a popular chant – but where did fans sing 'There's only *two* Gary Stevens'?

8. What was the usual Ibrox version of the Cockerel Chorus song 'Nice One Cyril' in the 1970s?

9. Which Rangers fan had a famous World Cup hit record in 1978?

10. Which familiar Ibrox tune was the basis for that song?

11. Who was praised in the 'Colin, Colin' chant of the late 1960s and early '70s?

12. What was the title of the single brought out to celebrate Rangers 1987 Premier League success?

13. Which Rangers player appeared on *Top of the Pops* with the Scottish World Cup squad in 1982?

14. Whose name did the Rangers fans sing to the tune of 'Daisy, Daisy'?

15. Since redevelopment, in which part of the ground has the main contingent of the Ibrox 'choir' congregated?

16. What was the title of the 1971 tribute album by the Rangers AFC Boys Club?

17. Which song do the Gers fans traditionally sing to the famous old Welsh tune 'Cwm Rhondda'?

18. Which opposing goalkeeper has had his name sung at Ibrox in recent seasons, after forming a good-natured rapport with the home fans?

19. During the 1970s, Rangers fans sang of which striker: 'Born is the King of Ibrox Park'?

20. Ally McCoist, Richard Gough and Mo Johnston all sang on Scotland's 1990 World Cup record. Can you remember its title?

— 29 —
WE'RE GOING TO WIN THE LEAGUE

John Greig with the Championship trophy – among others!

1. Have Rangers won more or less Scottish League Championships than Celtic?

2. In the first seven post-war seasons, the Gers took the League title four times – which team won in the other three years?

3. Who headed the equaliser at Easter Road which clinched the 1975 Championship?

4. That 1975 title was Rangers first League success in how many years?

5. Who was the leading goalscorer for the 1959 and 1961 Championship winning teams?

6. How many League titles did Rangers win under manager Bill Struth – 10, 14 or 18?

7. Which Lanarkshire team defeated champions Rangers before 63,000 Ibrox fans on the last day of the 1974–75 season?

8. Who skippered the 1949 'Treble' side?

9. Between 1966 and 1974, how many times did Rangers finish runners-up to Celtic in the League?

10. Which full-back played in all 34 League games of the 1962–63 Championship season?

11. Who was the top goalscorer of the 1974–75 side?

12. Rangers secured four League titles between 1956 and 1961 – which team won the other two?

13. Can you name either of the ever-presents in the side which won the 'Treble' in 1963–64?

14. And who finished that season as the club's leading scorer?

15. Which League did Rangers win six times during World War II?

16. Airdrie were the only side to beat the Gers twice during 1974–75 – which Edinburgh team inflicted their only other League defeat that season?

17. In which year did Rangers first win the Premier League title?

18. Which team finished runners-up to the Ibrox men in the Championships of 1961, 1963 and 1964?

19. Between 1980 and 1986, what was Rangers' highest end-of-season position in the Premier League?

20. On Scottish Cup Final day in 1968, the Gers saw their Championship hopes dashed when which team triumphed 3–2 at Ibrox?

— 30 —
BARCELONA '72

Rangers take the lead in Barcelona – see question 15

1. Which French side did Rangers defeat in the first round of their 1971–72 European Cup-Winners' Cup campaign?

2. What major mistake, later corrected by UEFA, did the referee make at the end of the second round, second leg game with Sporting Lisbon?

3. Who scored Rangers third and decisive away goal in that same match?

4. Which striker hit four goals over the two matches with Sporting?

5. Do you know who scored in both legs for the Portuguese club?

6. Who was the Rangers centre-half who tragically broke his leg in Lisbon?

7. Who scored the Ibrox goal which knocked out Italian Cup holders Torino in the quarter-finals?

8. Rangers met Bayern Munich in the semi-finals. Which West German international full-back shot the Bundesliga side ahead after 23 minutes of the Munich first leg?

9. Who struck for Gers in the first minute of the return match at Ibrox?

10. And which European debutant notched the vital second goal in Rangers' 2–0 victory?

11. Which key player was missing from the Scottish Cup holders' line-up that night?

12. Can you name the Barcelona stadium in which Gers defeated Moscow Dynamo to win the 1972 Cup-Winners' Cup?

13. How many Ibrox fans were estimated to have been in the 35,000 crowd that night?

14. What was the final score of the match?

15. Who fired Rangers ahead after 24 minutes?

16. And who was their other scoring hero?

17. Which defender set up the first two goals?

18. Who was the unfortunate player who missed the Final after sustaining an ankle injury in training?

19. And can you remember who took his position for the game?

20. Why was the Final not shown 'live' on TV in Scotland?

— 31 —
ON THE WING

Mark Walters shows his skills

1. In which English city was winger Mark Walters born?

2. How many League Championship medals did Davie Cooper win at Ibrox?

3. On which flank did he prefer to play?

4. Which famous Rangers winger starred in Scotland's 'Wembley Wizards' team which defeated England 5–1 in 1928?

5. Who wore numbers 7 and 11 in the 1967 European Cup-Winners' Cup Final side?

6. Which winger scored six goals against Falkirk in 1962 while playing in the centre-forward position?

7. In October 1972, this former Ayr United winger joined Rangers in an exchange deal. Can you name him?

8. Which winger scored direct from a corner in Gers' 4–2 win at Dumbarton of December 1984?

9. From which club was Willie Johnston re-signed in August 1980?

10. Who played on the right wing in the Cup-Winners' Cup triumph of 1972?

11. Which team did Davie Wilson join in 1967?

12. And who was the Swedish international who arrived at Ibrox as part of that deal?

13. In August 1987, which wide player made his Rangers debut as a substitute at Parkhead, only three days after scoring against the Gers in a Skol Cup match?

14. From which Second Division club was Ted McMinn signed in October 1984?

15. What nationality was 1950s winger Johnny Hubbard?

16. Tommy McLean won a League Championship medal at which club as an 18-year-old?

17. Against which team did Mark Walters notch a Hampden double in the Skol Cup semi-final shown 'live' on TV in September 1988?

18. Which Rangers winger was tragically killed in a home accident in March 1978?

19. With which club did Alex Scott win English League and Cup medals after leaving Ibrox in February 1963?

20. Which wingman scored the more goals for Rangers – Davie Wilson or Willie Johnston?

— 32 —
BRING ON THE CELTIC

The ball's in the Celtic net – again!

1. Who headed Rangers' goal in the 1–1 draw against Celtic at Parkhead in August 1989?

2. Which goalkeeper made his Old Firm debut in that match?

3. Rangers and Celtic fought out a highly-entertaining 4–4 draw in March 1986 – who scored twice for Gers?

4. Can you remember who opened the scoring for Celtic?

5. Who bagged two goals in the 5–1 thrashing of Celtic in August 1988?

6. And which other striker scored that day, in his first Old Firm match?

7. Who fired Rangers 2–1 ahead with a screaming shot just before half-time?

8. Can you name the unlucky 'keeper who was beaten five times?

9. Rangers lost 4–2 to Celtic at Ibrox in the last game of the 1982–83 season – what was the half-time score?

10. Who were the two Rangers ordered off in a 1–1 Parkhead draw of May 1985?

11. Who was making his Ibrox debut when he scored a dramatic late equaliser in the controversial Old Firm match of October 1987?

12. Who scored the winning goal in Rangers first-ever Premier League victory at Parkhead?

13. Which Celtic defender handled the ball to concede a vital penalty in Rangers' 3–0 win of April 1990?

14. Can you remember who converted the kick?

15. Which midfielder scored the only goal of the 'live' Old Firm match in August 1986?

16. In November 1985, Rangers put some indifferent League form behind them to score a resounding victory over Celtic at Ibrox – what was the result?

17. Which full-back hit Rangers only reply in their 2–1 defeat at Ibrox in March 1988?

18. Where did Rangers play their home matches against Celtic during the 1978–79 season?

19. Who was booked for excessively celebrating his first goal against Celtic in November 1989?

20. Who is Rangers' leading goalscorer in Old Firm Premier League games?

— 33 —
D. J.

Derek in action during the '70s

1. What age was Derek Johnstone when he headed the only goal of the 1970 Old Firm League Cup Final?

2. In which year did Derek win both the Scottish PFA and Football Writers' Player of the Year award?

3. Which English club did he join in 1983?

4. Which Rangers manager made Johnstone captain of the side?

5. Against which of the home countries did he make his first appearance for Scotland in May 1973?

6. And in what position did he play in that debut game?

7. Which team did Derek support as a boy?

8. Against which Edinburgh club did he net four times in Rangers' 5–3 victory of December 1978?

9. In which year did he miss the Scottish Cup Final because of a knee injury?

10. Which club did Derek manage for eight months of the 1986–87 season?

11. In which country was he ordered off in European matches of 1976 and 1977?

12. During the 1983-84 season, Johnstone played against Rangers while on loan to which Premier League club?

13. In how many World Cup finals matches did he play?

14. Against which Fife team, now in Division Two, did he make his Rangers debut in September 1970?

15. What number of jersey did Derek wear in Rangers' 1972 European Cup-Winners' Cup victory?

16. In January 1985 Derek returned to Ibrox, but in his first game back, Rangers crashed 5–1 away to which team?

17. How many Scotland caps did he win – 14, 24 or 34?

18. During 1988–89, Derek helped present *Sportscene*'s preview programme with a former Old Firm rival – who was that?

19. Do you know how many Scottish Cup Final goals he scored altogether?

20. In which year did the big man play his last match for Rangers?

— 34 —
IBROX STADIUM

The home of Scotland's champions

1. Which was the first new stand completed in the Ibrox redevelopment which began in 1978?

2. Which other Glasgow club played some of their home matches at Ibrox during the 1908–09 season?

3. The greatest ever Ibrox crowd, 118,567, watched which team play Rangers in January 1939?

4. Whose portrait overlooks the marble staircase in the entrance hall?

5. Which stand was officially opened before a 1980 friendly against Spurs?

6. What did the North Enclosure become in 1973?

7. In February 1991, Scotland played their first international match at Ibrox in over 50 years. Who were their opponents?

8. Which boxer defended his World Lightweight title at Ibrox in 1980?

9. On what street is the Main Stand situated?

10. The final of which national semi-professional tournament was played at Ibrox during the early 1980s?

11. Which team played Rangers in the first ever floodlit match at the stadium in 1953?

12. Which stand was first used in the game against Celtic of 19th September 1981?

13. Can you remember the score that day?

14. In which part of the ground are away fans usually housed?

15. Before redevelopment in 1978, which was the only club ground in Britain with a bigger capacity than Ibrox?

16. What are the five seat colours in the new stands?

17. In which year did Rangers install their 'electric blanket'?

18. What has been both the 'Rangers Social Club' and 'Morley's Night Spot'?

19. What is the name of the former greyhound racing venue, adjacent to Ibrox and until recently used as a training ground by Rangers?

20. Rangers generally prefer to shoot towards which stand during the first half of home matches?

— 35 —
WORLD CUP
GERS

Mo Johnston on target in the 1990 World Cup

1. Who were the three Rangers in Scotland's 1990 World Cup squad?

2. Ian Ferguson played in two World Cup qualifying games during 1989 – can you name either of the countries he faced?

3. Who was the only Rangers player to appear in the 1982 World Cup finals?

4. How many goals did Colin Stein score against Cyprus in 1969?

5. Do you know which other Ranger also netted in Scotland's 8–0 win?

6. Who was the Ibrox representative in the 1974 World Cup?

7. Which Ranger took part in the Oceania/South America World Cup qualifying play-off in October 1989?

8. Davie Cooper scored a vital goal in a 1985 play-off match – against which country?

9. How many Rangers players were in England's 1990 World Cup squad?

10. Which former Ibrox hero was sent home from the 1978 finals after failing a drugs test?

11. Where did Richard Gough hit two goals for Scotland in a World Cup qualifier of February 1989?

12. Who set up Gary Lineker for England's first goal of the 1986 finals?

13. Ian Durrant made one brief appearance in Scotland's last qualifying campaign – against which country did he play?

14. Which Rangers defender played in the 1978 World Cup finals?

15. Ally McCoist only started one game of the 1990 tournament in Italy – which one?

16. In November 1984, which Ranger netted twice in a World Cup qualifying match in Lisbon?

17. Ian McMillan won his only cap as a Ranger in Scotland's 4–0 defeat by which country in 1961?

18. Who was the first Ibrox player to score in the World Cup finals?

19. Can you name the Rangers man in Canada's 1986 World Cup squad?

20. In how many matches did Richard Gough play during the 1990 finals in Italy?

— 36 —
CHAMPIONIS –
1988–89

Rangers in action against St Mirren – see question 12

1. Rangers defeated Hearts 4–0 at Ibrox in April 1989 to clinch the Premier League Championship. Can you name the two Englishmen who each scored twice that day?

2. Where did Neale Cooper score on his Rangers debut in October 1988?

3. Which defender scored his only goal of the season with a tremendous left-foot strike at Tannadice in February?

4. Against which team did Rangers record their highest League victory of 1988–89?

5. Who was making his Premier League debut when he scored in the opening game of the season at Hamilton?

6. In November 1988, in David Murray's first match as chairman of the club, Rangers defeated Aberdeen 1–0 at Ibrox. Which defender scored the winner?

7. Against which team did Mel Sterland score on his Ibrox debut?

8. Who scored his only goal of the season with a delightful left-foot chip for the winning goal against Hibs at Ibrox in December 1988?

9. After beating Celtic 4–1 on 3rd January, Rangers went down 2–1 to which team on the following Saturday?

10. Can you remember who scored an unfortunate diving own goal in that game?

11. Which £25,000 signing headed his first goal for the club in the 1–1 draw against St Mirren at Love Street in October?

12. Which ex-St Mirren player netted in two matches against his old team?

13. Who headed Rangers ahead after only five minutes of the crunch Old Firm game at Parkhead on 1st April?

14. There was some dubiety over who scored Gers' second goal in their 2–1 win that day. Who was eventually credited with nodding Ian Ferguson's free-kick over the line?

15. In the second half, Chris Woods made a great penalty save from which Celtic player?

16. During 1988–89, the Gers were unbeaten in their first eight League matches. Which team inflicted their first defeat in October?

17. Who were the two players ordered off in Hearts' 2–0 victory over the Gers in December?

18. Against which team did Ally McCoist make a scoring return in January after being out for 13 matches?
19. Who drew 0–0 at Aberdeen to enable Rangers to take the Championship against Hearts in April?
20. On the last day of the season, Aberdeen spoiled the party by winning at Ibrox – can you remember the score?

— 37 —
PASTA AND
BOVRIL

The Gers shock star-studded Juventus in 1978

1. Which Italian city did Rangers visit twice in European competition during the 1970s?

2. In 1957, which Italian side became the first team to win at Ibrox in a European tie when they defeated the Gers 4–1?

3. Rangers lost the first-ever European Cup-Winners' Cup Final to which club?

4. In what way was that Final different from today's Cup-Winners' Cup Finals?

5. Which Italian team defeated Rangers on their way to lifting the 1965 European Cup?

6. Do you know who they beat in that season's Final?

7. How many of Italy's 1978 World Cup squad were in the Juventus team beaten by Rangers in that year's European Cup first round?

8. Which famous goalkeeper played in both legs for the Turin club?

9. Can you name either of the Gers' scorers in their 2–0 second-leg victory?

10. Inter Milan eliminated Rangers from the 1984–85 UEFA Cup – what was the aggregate score?

11. The first leg was played in Milan's Guiseppe Meazza Stadium – by what name was it better known at that time?

12. Which Irishman played for Inter that night?

13. Who was the star West German striker who hit the third goal of their 3–0 win?

14. Inter's vital away goal at Ibrox was scored by a veteran Italian international forward nicknamed 'The Big Pin' – can you name him?

15. Which defender played his last match for Rangers that night?

16. What nationality was Fiorentina winger Kurt Hamrin who scored a magnificent second goal in the 1961 Cup-Winners' Cup Final second-leg match?

17. Who made his 50th European appearance for Rangers in a 1972 Cup-Winners' match against Torino?

18. Which striker scored in both legs of the 1965 European Cup tie with Inter?

19. What is the unusual colour of Fiorentina's jersey in which they played the first leg of the 1961 Cup-Winners' Cup Final at Ibrox?

20. Which famous international defender, a member of the Juventus team defeated by Rangers in 1978, was killed in a car crash in September 1989?

— 38 —
COOP

'Super Cooper' prepares to unlock another defence

1. Davie Cooper won his first medal with Rangers in which competition?

2. How much did Rangers pay Clydebank for Davie in June 1977?

3. Who is the leading Scottish League official who signed him for the Bankies?

4. During his time at Kilbowie, Cooper played against Rangers in a four-game marathon League Cup tie – in how many of these matches did he score?

5. In August 1979, Davie beat four Celtic defenders to score a Hampden wonder-goal in the final of which competition?

6. Against which team did he score his only Scottish Cup Final goal?

7. Davie made his international debut against which South American country in 1979?

8. Which Scotland manager gave him his first full cap?

9. In which year did he score Rangers' winning goal in the Skol Cup Final?

10. After whom was Davie given the nickname 'Albert' by his Ibrox team-mates?

11. Where did he convert a vital penalty kick for Scotland in September 1985?

12. Did Davie play a full match during the 1986 World Cup finals in Mexico?

13. What was unusual about Coop's goal in the Old Firm League match of October 1982?

14. Where did Rangers lose 3–1 in Davie's first Premier League match for the club in August 1977?

15. In May 1985, he was ordered off at Parkhead for a retaliatory foul on which Celtic player?

16. Against which British country did he score his first goal for Scotland in 1984?

17. Did Coop ever play in a Scotland-England match?

18. In May 1990, he had to make an unfortunate withdrawal from Scotland's World Cup squad – which former Ibrox team-mate took his place?
19. Which French side did Rangers play in his testimonial match?
20. What was Davie's last match for Rangers?

— 39 —
CUP OF WOE

The 1991 cup nightmare begins at Parkhead

1. Who scored the two goals for Celtic which ended Rangers' Scottish Cup hopes in March 1991?

2. Which Second Division team rocked Scottish football by knocking Rangers out of the Cup in 1967?

3. Who kept goal for them that day?

4. Which team ended the Gers' interest in the 1988 Scottish Cup with a 2–0 fourth round victory?

5. Which Ranger was ordered off in that tie?

6. Can you remember the Hamilton Accies goalscorer in their sensational defeat of Rangers in January 1987?

7. Which team eliminated Rangers from the Scottish Cup in two consecutive seasons during the mid-1980s?

8. In March 1961, who scored Motherwell's fourth goal in their 5–2 third round replay victory at Ibrox?

9. Rangers went out of the 1986 Scottish Cup at Tynecastle. What was the score that day?

10. Can you name either of the Gers' scorers?

11. Who received his marching orders after an incident with Hearts' Gary Mackay in the 72nd minute?

12. Which former Ibrox star netted Hearts' first goal in that game?

13. Who scored Dundee's winner in their 3–2 quarter-final replay victory at Ibrox in March 1984?

14. And which former Dundee player was sent off?

15. What was the score of the first game at Dens Park?

16. Which team defeated Rangers in the 1972 Scottish Cup semi-final replay after having been eliminated by the Ibrox men in the three previous seasons?

17. Do you know who scored Berwick's winner in 1967?

18. Can you name either of the forwards who played their last match for Rangers in that Berwick defeat?

19. Which team ended Gers' interest in the 1975 Scottish Cup when goals from Graham and Davidson gave them a 2–1 third round replay victory at Ibrox?

20. Who scored the only goal of the Rangers-Dundee fourth round tie of February 1985?

— 40 —
ANYWHERE,
EVERYWHERE

Dynamo Kiev crash out of the European Cup at Ibrox –
see question 11

1. In which Polish town did Rangers record a 4–2 victory in the 1988–89 UEFA Cup competition?

2. Who scored twice for the Gers' in that game?

3. Which Russian team played a famous friendly at Ibrox in 1945?

4. Against which side did Rangers record their highest-ever aggregate victory in Europe?

5. What was that record score?

6. Who is the famous Portuguese international striker who netted FC Porto's winner in the 1983 European Cup-Winners' Cup tie in Oporto?

7. In 1986–87, Rangers defeated Ilves Tampere 4–0 at Ibrox – but what was the result of the return leg in Finland?

8. Who were the 1956 French Champions who were Rangers' first-ever European opponents?

9. Which is the only Austrian team which the Gers have faced in European competition?

10. Where did the Ibrox men crash 3–0 in a 1981 Cup-Winners' Cup tie?

11. Who were Rangers' scorers in the famous 2–0 victory over Dynamo Kiev in September 1987?

12. Which Norwegian side, later managed by Davie Hay, did the Gers eliminate from the 1979 Cup-Winners' tournament?

13. Who was the Irishman who played for Porto against Rangers in 1983?

14. Which Ibrox striker scored his only European goal for the club in that tie?

15. Which French team knocked out Rangers on their way to reaching the 1976 European Cup Final?

16. Can you name either of the Gers' men who netted in the 2–1 Ibrox victory over Steaua Bucharest in the 1988 European Cup quarter-finals?

17. Which star striker notched the vital away goal which took Steaua through?

18. Which Irish side did Rangers eliminate from European competition in 1975 and 1984?

19. From which city do 1977 Cup-Winners' Cup opponents Young Boys come?

20. Who scored Rangers' first-ever European Cup goal in the 1956 match against Nice?

— 41 —
ONCE A RANGER

Davie MacKinnon – see question 6

1. Which former Rangers star played for the Football League against the Rest of the World in August 1987?

2. During the 1978–79 season, ex-Ibrox winger Willie Henderson made a brief comeback to Scottish Football with his hometown club – who was that?

3. Can you name either of the former Rangers who won English divisional championship medals in 1988–89?

4. Which club did Ralph Brand manage in the 1972–73 season?

5. Which one-time Ibrox striker moved from Barnsley to Scarborough in November 1989?

6. Which club did Davie MacKinnon help to promotion from Division Two in 1989–90?

7. Who was the former Rangers centre-forward who won a Scottish Cup medal in Aberdeen's 3–1 defeat of Celtic in 1970?

8. Which ex-Ranger managed Albion Rovers to the 1989 Second Division title?

9. Where was Alex Miller's first managerial post?

10. Which member of Rangers' 1970 youth team went on to win European Cup medals with Nottingham Forest?

11. After leaving Ibrox in 1982, Colin Jackson played for which two teams before retiring?

12. Which ex-Ranger was Scottish Footballer of the Year in 1986?

13. Can you name the one-time Ibrox coach who led Blackburn Rovers into the English Second Division play-offs in three successive seasons from 1988 to 1990?

14. For which club did Trevor Francis play in 1990–91?

15. Which former Rangers striker helped Inverness Caley knock Airdrie out of the 1990 Scottish Cup?

16. Which ex-Ger went on to win an English Second Division Championship medal with Leeds United?

17. Gordon Dalziel notched 28 goals for which club during the 1990–91 season?

18. Who was the former Ibrox player who appeared in the 1989–90 Bundesliga for Bayer Uerdingen?

19. Once on Rangers' books and part of Dundee's Championship-winning squad of 1962, he is however best known as assistant to Andy Roxburgh in the 1990 World Cup. Who is he?
20. Ex-Ibrox striker Iain Ferguson played against Rangers in the colours of *two* other Premier League clubs during 1990–91. Can you name the two clubs?

— 42 —
JUST A MO!

Mo Jo – Rangers' most sensational signing of all time?

1. Where did Mo Johnston make his Rangers debut in a testimonial match of July 1989?

2. What was his first senior club?

3. Who was the manager who signed him for Watford in 1983?

4. In November 1990, he scored his first goal at Parkhead for Rangers. What was the result of that match?

5. Against which country did Mo make his Scotland debut in February 1984?

6. In November that year, he scored two vital goals in Scotland's 3–1 World Cup win over which nation?

7. How many goals did Mo score against Celtic in his first season with Rangers?

8. In January 1985, he missed a penalty in the Old Firm clash at Ibrox – which Gers 'keeper saved it?

9. Against which team did Mo make his Premier League debut for Partick Thistle in August 1981?

10. While with Watford, he played in the 1984 FA Cup Final against Everton – what was the result of that game?

11. In September 1989, Mo headed his first Premier League goal for Rangers – against which team?

12. Where did he notch his first double for the Gers, in September 1990?

13. Who was the former Belgian World Cup skipper who played with Mo at Nantes?

14. How many goals did he score in the qualifying matches for the 1990 World Cup?

15. Against which country did Mo score with a penalty in the World Cup finals?

16. Where did he score his first League goal for Thistle in October 1981?

17. Can you name his childhood friend who played against him for Hibs during 1990–91?

18. Who is the agent who helped clinch Mo's transfer to Rangers?

19. What number did he wear during his first season at Ibrox?
20. Mo bagged how many Premier League goals during 1990–91
– 11, 13 or 15?

— 43 —
LIFTING THE LEAGUE CUP

Ally McCoist on target in the 1984 Final

1. Who was the Rangers substitute who chipped Dundee United goalkeeper Hamish McAlpine to score a dramatic late winner in the 1981 League Cup Final?

2. Which team did Rangers defeat 4–0 in the first-ever League Cup Final in 1947?

3. The Gers lost 2–1 to Celtic in the 1982 Final – who netted their goal from a free-kick?

4. Which Edinburgh side, then in the First Division, had they defeated in that season's semi-finals?

5. Who headed a last-minute winner in the 1979 League Cup Final against Aberdeen?

6. Can you remember which Dons defender was ordered off in that match?

7. And who was the Ibrox man involved in the incident?

8. In a League Cup tie of August 1972, St Mirren stunned Rangers with a 4–1 victory at Ibrox – who scored all four goals for the Buddies?

9. Which long-serving defender skippered the Rangers side which defeated Celtic 1–0 in the 1970 League Cup Final?

10. Regular captain John Greig missed that match through injury – which youngster took his place in the team?

11. In the 1981 League Cup Final, who equalised for Rangers after Ralph Milne had shot Dundee United ahead?

12. Which team had the Gers trounced 8–1 in a sectional tie of that season's competition?

13. Who was the former Ibrox goalkeeper who saved a penalty for Forfar in a first round, second leg League Cup match of August 1980?

14. The last time that Rangers met Celtic in the semi-final of a national competition was in the 1978 League Cup – can you remember the result?

15. Which team ended the Gers' League Cup hopes in both the 1979–80 and 80–81 seasons?

16. Who was the Celt who hit a hat-trick against Rangers in the 1973–74 semi-final?

17. Which Second Division side did Gers defeat 5–0 in the 1964 League Cup Final?

18. Which ex-Ranger has more League Cup medals than any other Scottish player?

19. Which team thwarted Rangers' Treble hopes in 1962–63 by defeating them 3–2 in the League Cup semi-final?

20. Can you remember the Celtic player whose own goal decided the 1978 semi-final?

— 44 —
IN THE
HOT SEAT

Walter Smith points the way ahead

1. Who is the only Rangers manager to have won the 'Treble' twice?

2. Who was manager of the victorious European Cup-Winners' Cup team of 1972?

3. What was the first trophy won by Graeme Souness as Rangers boss?

4. Which Ibrox manager was sacked while Rangers were top of the League in November 1967?

5. Which other Glasgow club did Bill Struth leave to join Rangers in 1914?

6. Where did Jock Wallace go after leaving Ibrox in 1986?

7. Whom did Willie Waddell replace as manager in 1969?

8. Which club had Waddell guided to the 1965 League Championship?

9. Who was the Rangers goalkeeper who went on to become Scotland manager?

10. In November 1983, two leading Scottish managers turned down the chance of moving to Ibrox – can you name them?

11. Which English club did Scot Symon boss before joining Rangers in June 1954?

12. Who was effectively the first manager of Rangers?

13. Which Scottish club did both George Young and Bobby Shearer manage?

14. Which club did Walter Smith leave to come to Ibrox?

15. Whose one match in charge of the Rangers' team ended in a 2–1 defeat at Clydebank in April 1986?

16. Who was caretaker boss after John Greig left the club in 1983?

17. Do you know which Ibrox manager was a cricket international for Scotland?

18. And which one was a former jungle fighter?

19. Which club did Davie White manage after he was sacked by Rangers?

20. Who was appointed Scotland boss in November 1960, while still a player at Ibrox?

— 45 —
1986–87 –
THAT CHAMPIONSHIP
SEASON

That vital goal from Terry Butcher at Pittodrie

1. Which Edinburgh team beat Rangers on the opening day of the 1986–87 season?

2. The Gers notched their first League win with a Wednesday-night victory over which side?

3. Which team came from 2–0 down to win 3–2 at Ibrox on the second Saturday of the season?

4. And who was the ex-Ranger who headed their winner that day?

5. After losing to Aberdeen in November, Rangers were how many points behind leaders Celtic?

6. A brilliant run of results saw them go top after beating which team 2–0 at Ibrox in January 1987?

7. Rangers set themselves up for the Championship with a 3–0 Ibrox victory over Hearts in April – who scored all three goals?

8. Which team beat Celtic at Parkhead to allow Rangers to clinch the title at Pittodrie on 2nd May?

9. Who scored Aberdeen's equaliser in the 1–1 draw that day?

10. Rangers' last game of the season was against one of the 1987 Cup Finalists – who were they?

11. Who scored a marvellous solo goal in the 1–1 draw at Tynecastle in October 1986?

12. Graeme Souness fired home his first Scottish Premier League goal against which goalkeeper in September?

13. Who made a scoring Ibrox debut, in the No.2 shirt, against Dundee United in Gers' last match of 1986?

14. Who wore the No.5 jersey in 42 Premier League matches, despite playing mainly at right-back?

15. Can you remember who converted two penalties for Celtic in Rangers' 3–1 reverse at Parkhead in April 1987?

16. Who scored the Gers' goal in their 1–1 draw at Parkhead, one week after they had beaten Celtic in the Skol Cup Final?

17. Chris Woods played in 42 Premier League matches during 1986–87. In how many did he keep a clean sheet – 15, 20 or 25?

18. Which striker scored his first League goal at Hamilton in August and his second at Clydebank in April?

19. Who was Rangers' only ever-present in the 1986–87 season?

20. When Ally McCoist netted his first goal against Hearts in April, he broke a 20-year-old record held by Jim Forrest. Do you know what that was?

— 46 —
GREIGY

John in his last season as a player

1. Where was John Greig born?
2. In which year did he make his debut for Rangers?
3. Which midfield star did he replace in his first game?
4. John established himself in the Rangers first team during a close-season tour of which country in 1962?
5. In which year did he make his Scotland debut?
6. In November 1965, Greig scored a famous World Cup goal for Scotland against which country?
7. In which year did he win his first Scottish Footballer of the Year award?
8. How many goals did John score for Rangers – 100, 130 or 160?
9. In which position did he play in the 'Treble' teams of 1976 and 1978?
10. Although against club policy, John sported a beard in the 1972 European Cup-Winners' Cup Final – why was this?
11. What was special about his goal against Clyde in March 1974?
12. In September that year, he scored two European goals against which Turkish side at Ibrox?
13. In which year was Greig appointed Rangers manager?
14. How many times did the Gers reach the Scottish Cup Final during his five-year reign as boss?
15. How many caps did John win altogether – 24, 34 or 44?
16. Who succeeded him as Scotland captain?
17. Who did Rangers play in John's testimonial match in 1978?
18. Can you remember the score?
19. What award did John receive from The Queen in 1977?
20. Do you know which team he supported as a boy?

— 47 —
CELEBRITY
BEARS

Who's the Rangers star with Rod? – see question 17

1. Can you name the lead singer of 'Wet Wet Wet' who is a self-confessed Rangers fan?

2. Which cricket superstar, a fan of both Rangers and Chelsea, took in the Ibrox match against Hibs in October 1989?

3. Which member of the Royal Family presented John Greig with the 1973 Scottish Cup?

4. Who is the former Rangers player who became World Indoor Bowls Champion?

5. Can you name the former host of *Opportunity Knocks* who attended the Rangers-Falkirk Scottish Cup replay of February 1972?

6. Which international singing star watched the Old Firm match of January 1987?

7. He was rather disappointed with the score that day – can you remember what it was?

8. Which Labour leader was part of the 18,000 crowd at the Rangers-St Mirren match of November 1981?

9. Who was the *Miss World* supremo pictured wearing a Rangers scarf in 1977?

10. Can you name the famous Russian Prime Minister who watched Rangers play Kilmarnock at Rugby Park in 1967?

11. Who was the young snooker star who saw his team, Hearts, draw 0–0 at Ibrox in February 1990?

12. Which comedian was chairman of Sandy Jardine's 1982 testimonial committee?

13. Who made the Scottish Cup draw at Ibrox in March 1990?

14. Can you name the guitarist who made the 1987 'Championi' single?

15. Which British Prime Minister presented Derek Johnstone with his 1978 Scottish Footballer of the Year award?

16. With which team did former Rumanian dictator's son Nicolae Ceausescu visit Ibrox in 1988?

17. Rod Stewart once swapped a gold disc LP for one of which Ranger's international caps?

18. Before Mrs Thatcher in 1990, which was the last Conservative leader to come to Ibrox?

19. Which late, Rangers-daft comedian once said that he'd 'like to buy Parkhead and run the Blue Trains through it'?

20. Can you name the two former Celtic players, with over 160 caps between them, who were Rangers fans as youngsters?

— 48 —
OVER
THE BORDER

Chelsea go behind on their 1986 visit to Ibrox

1. In 1961, Rangers defeated the English Cup holders in the semi-finals of the European Cup-Winners' Cup – who were they?

2. Which English club played at Ibrox as part of the 1973 centenary celebrations?

3. What was the aggregate score when Spurs beat Rangers in the 1962–63 Cup-Winners' Cup?

4. Which TV presenter scored in both legs for the Londoners?

5. How far did Spurs progress in that season's competition?

6. In 1975, Rangers played a trouble-hit friendly away to which English Midlands club?

7. The Gers met Leeds United in the 1967–68 Fairs Cup – at what stage of the tournament?

8. Who was the Scotsman who skippered Leeds in those games?

9. Which Scot netted Leeds' second goal in their 2–0 second leg victory at Elland Road?

10. Which team played Rangers in the new Ibrox Stadium's official opening match in December 1981?

11. Rangers won the 1987 Dubai Super Cup after defeating English Champions Everton in a penalty shoot-out, but what was the result of the match?

12. Who missed a penalty for the Gers in the 1969 Fairs Cup semi-final first leg against Newcastle at Ibrox?

13. Can you name the Irish international goalkeeper, later a manager of the Geordie club, who saved it?

14. Both of Newcastle's goals in their second leg win were scored by Scots – can you name either player?

15. In August 1986, new manager Graeme Souness took Rangers to London to play Spurs in Paul Miller's testimonial match – what was the score that day?

16. Which small English club shocked the Gers in the 1980–81 Anglo-Scottish Cup?

17. And who was the former Ibrox player who netted twice for the Third Division outfit?

18. Who kept goal for Leeds against Rangers in 1968 and later played in the World Cup for Scotland?

19. How did 43,177 fans see the second leg of that 1968 tie without travelling to Leeds?

20. In that match, two future international managers were in direct opposition – can you name them?

— 49 —
THE NAME
GAME

Ray Wilkins – see question 5

1. Which 1960s Rangers star was known as 'The Wee Prime Minister'?

2. What was Willie Johnston's nickname at Ibrox?

3. Which goalkeeper was dubbed 'The Girvan Lighthouse'?

4. Who was 'Meek'?

5. What was Ray Wilkins' nickname during his time with Rangers?

6. 'Doddie' was an Ibrox star of the 1970s – what's his real name?

7. Who did Gers fans call 'The Tin Man'?

8. Which South African-born forward of the '50s was known as 'The Rhino'?

9. What was the nickname of winger Quinton Young?

10. 'Dozy' captained Rangers' Scottish Cup winning team of 1981 – who is he?

11. Which full-back was dubbed 'Rambo' by the Ibrox supporters?

12. What was Colin Jackson's nickname?

13. Which Rangers legend was known as 'The Wee Blue Devil'?

14. Can you name the 1960s striker who was called 'Dandy'?

15. 'Jazzer' played for Rangers from 1980 to 1983 – who is he?

16. By what name is Gers' assistant kit manager George Soutar known at Ibrox?

17. Which defender was known as 'Jaws'?

18. 'Drinks' notched 19 goals for Gers in 1988–89 – what's his full name?

19. What was the nickname of Irish international full-back Billy McCandless?

20. Who was known as 'Corky' and why?

— 50 —
BOOKED!

'Robbo' – see question 19

1. Whose autobiography is entitled *True Blue*?

2. In which year did John Allan write the first history of Rangers FC – 1923, 1933 or 1943?

3. Which commentator recently wrote a book on famous Rangers-Celtic matches entitled *Blue & Green*?

4. In his book *Rangers Greats*, who does journalist Dixon Blackstock consider to be the greatest Rangers player he has ever seen?

5. In which year did the *Rangers News* first appear?

6. Which Ibrox player was the subject of the book *On the Wing*?

7. Do you know the title of Graeme Souness's autobiography?

8. Which annual feature book on Rangers was first produced in 1969?

9. Can you name the Australian author who produced a highly controversial book on the Old Firm in 1984?

10. What is the title of Terry Butcher's book?

11. To whom does the book *Legend* refer?

12. Who was co-author of Mo Johnston's autobiography *Mo*?

13. What is the title of Trevor Steven and Gary Stevens' joint autobiography?

14. In 1979, who wrote of *Rangers: My Team*?

15. What was the title of the centenary history of Rangers, published in 1973?

16. Which Ibrox manager had a spell working as a journalist?

17. During 1988–89, Graeme Souness teamed up with Ken Gallacher to produce a fascinating account of the season – what was the book's title?

18. Which Ranger was the author of the 1968 book *A Captain's Part*?

19. What was Graham Roberts' autobiography called?

20. Can you remember the title of Chick Young's 1987 book on the Rangers revival?

OUT OF THE BLUE

An undercover operation for Rangers – see question 18

1. Who is the only Rangers player to have been a member of three 'Treble' winning teams?

2. What is Rangers' lowest-ever finishing position in the Scottish League?

3. Which two Ibrox team-mates were in opposition in the Scotland-Northern Ireland match of May 1983?

4. Which Brazilian club won the Rangers International pre-season tournament in August 1987?

5. In 1961, why did the Gers play the home leg of their European Cup tie against Vorwaerts Frankfurt in Malmo, Sweden?

6. Two teams put five goals past Rangers during the 1980s – can you remember which two?

7. Who was the *Rangers News* Player of the Year for 1990–91?

8. In January 1971, an Old Firm Select played Scotland in aid of the Ibrox disaster fund – who scored for the Select?

9. Which is the only season in Rangers' history in which they lost more League matches than they won?

10. During the 1982–83 season, who played in the English FA Cup Final after having earlier played for Rangers in the Final of the Scottish League Cup?

11. Which Scottish international striker notched four goals in Dundee's 5–1 win at Ibrox in November 1961?

12. Who holds the record for most all-time League appearances for Rangers?

13. In May 1986, which team did the Gers defeat 2–0 in Graeme Souness' first match in charge at Ibrox?

14. Which Ranger was 1975 Scottish Footballer of the Year?

15. About what did Dynamo Kiev complain after losing their European Cup tie at Ibrox in September 1987?

16. Rangers' record victory came against Blairgowrie in the 1934 Scottish Cup – do you know the score?

17. Who were the two cousins who, between them, netted all five Gers goals in the 1963–64 League Cup Final?

18. Which indoor competition did the Gers win in 1984 and 1989?

19. Who was the Icelandic international who played for Rangers during the 1960s?

20. In terms of percentage of League matches won, who is the most successful post-war Rangers manager?

ANSWERS

1 RANGERS HOT SHOTS

1. Monaco
2. Andy Gray
3. Ally McCoist
4. Clydebank
5. Derek Parlane
6. Robert Fleck
7. Sandy Clark
8. Colin Stein
9. Neuchatel Xamax
10. Colin McAdam
11. Mark Walters
12. 'M & B'
13. Davie Mitchell
14. A holiday
15. Jim Forrest
16. The Glasgow Cup
17. Bob McPhail
18. Iain Ferguson
19. Torry Gillick
20. Kevin Drinkell

2 HAPPY NEW YEAR

1. Nigel Spackman
2. Graeme Souness and Graham Roberts
3. Robert Fleck
4. Mo Johnston
5. Chris Woods
6. Graham Roberts
7. Derek Johnstone
8. Jim Bett
9. Because of a blizzard
10. Mark Walters
11. Rangers
12. Mark Walters and Mark Hateley
13. John Greig
14. Mark Walters
15. Frank McAvennie
16. Kenny Black
17. Kevin Drinkell
18. Jimmy Millar
19. Johnstone, McLean and Parlane
20. Billy McNeill

3   SPANIARDS BY THE SCORE

1. Real Madrid
2. Tommy McLean
3. Sandy Jardine
4. Derek Johnstone
5. Mario Kempes
6. Atletico Osasuna
7. 2–0 to Bilbao
8. John Greig
9. Willie Johnston
10. Real Sociedad
11. John Toshack
12. 2–2
13. By the toss of a coin
14. Dave Smith
15. Ferenc Puskas
16. Billy Ritchie
17. Alfredo Di Stefano
18. Craig Paterson
19. Rainer Bonhof
20. Arsenal

4   *THREE IN A ROW – 1990–91*

1. Two
2. Mark Hateley
3. Celtic
4. Tannadice
5. John Spencer
6. Dundee United
7. Ally McCoist
8. Motherwell
9. Pieter Huistra
10. Hans Gillhaus
11. Trevor Steven
12. Scott Nisbet
13. Hibs
14. Sandy Robertson
15. Ian Ferguson
16. Motherwell
17. Nigel Spackman
18. Tom Cowan and John Brown
19. Michael Watt
20. Chris Woods and Gary Stevens

5 COMINGS AND GOINGS

1. Colin West
2. Spurs
3. Davie MacKinnon
4. Ally Dawson
5. Clyde
6. Preston
7. Avi Cohen
8. Bradford
9. Gordon Dalziel
10. Tom Leeman
11. Seville
12. Martin Henderson
13. Cammy Fraser
14. Kilmarnock
15. Davie Kirkwood
16. Jimmy Nicholl
17. Queen's Park Rangers
18. John Spencer
19. Coventry
20. Derek Johnstone, Davie MacKinnon, Andy Bruce, Billy Davies and Eric Ferguson

6 JUST CHAMPION! – 1989–90

1. Tannadice
2. Trevor Steven
3. November
4. Stuart Munro and Mo Johnston
5. Dunfermline
6. John Brown
7. St Mirren
8. Mark Walters and Ally McCoist
9. Bobby Russell
10. Six
11. Davie Dodds
12. Hibs
13. Tynecastle
14. Scott Nisbet
15. Arsenal
16. Derek Ferguson
17. Mo Johnston
18. Gary Stevens
19. Motherwell, Hearts, Dundee and St Mirren
20. Stuart Munro

7 THE YELLOW JERSEY

1. Easter Road
2. Stenhousemuir
3. Longest run without conceding a goal – 1,196 minutes
4. Israel
5. Norrie Martin
6. Jerry
7. Bobby Brown
8. Jim Stewart
9. Oldham
10. Peter McCloy
11. Erik Sorensen
12. Nicky Walker
13. Stewart Kennedy
14. West German
15. Billy Ritchie
16. Cricket
17. Stirling Albion
18. He was suspended
19. Jim Stewart
20. Motherwell

8   IN THE BEGINNING

1. 1872
2. Glasgow Green
3. McNeil
4. Queen's Park
5. The FA Cup
6. Kinning Park
7. Preston North End
8. Dumbarton
9. Celtic
10. All eighteen!
11. Because the fans had rioted
12. Andy Cunningham
13. Eight
14. The Glasgow Cup and the Glasgow Charity Cup
15. John Thomson
16. Arsenal
17. Third Lanark
18. Canada and the USA
19. Willie Waddell
20. 4–0

9 *AUF WIEDERSEHEN*

1. Cologne
2. Ian Durrant
3. Seven
4. Nuremberg
5. Fortuna
6. Danish
7. Harald Schumacher
8. Colin Stein
9. Borussia Dortmund
10. Franz Roth
11. 5–0 to Cologne
12. Mark Walters
13. Klaus Augenthaler
14. Alan McInally
15. Dieter Muller
16. Eintracht Frankfurt
17. Jupp Heynckes
18. Pierre Littbarski
19. Tommy McLean
20. Kevin Drinkell

10 SUPER ALLY

1. 1983
2. Sunderland
3. He became Rangers' leading post-war goalscorer
4. Derek Johnstone
5. St Johnstone
6. Motherwell
7. Holland
8. John Greig
9. Skol Cup in 1984
10. Hungary
11. 'Sportscene Personality of the Year'
12. Celtic
13. He had undergone a cartilage operation only a week earlier
14. Bohemians
15. The Glasgow Cup
16. Colin West
17. Sandy Clark
18. Norway
19. Alan Durban
20. No

11 UP FOR THE CUP

1. Once
2. Ian Redford
3. Hamish McAlpine
4. 0–0
5. Derek Johnstone
6. Tom Forsyth
7. John Greig
8. Jimmy Millar
9. Andy Penman
10. Davie Cooper
11. John MacDonald
12. Arthur Duncan
13. Partick Thistle
14. Jim Baxter
15. Davie Dodds
16. Morton
17. 42 seconds
18. 1966
19. St Mirren
20. Ally Dawson

12 DARK BLUE RANGERS

1. George Young
2. Stuart Munro
3. Richard Gough and Ian Ferguson
4. Colin Stein
5. Shearer and Caldow
6. Ally Dawson
7. Ian Durrant
8. Sammy Cox
9. Alex MacDonald
10. 1–1
11. Scott (3), Brand (2) and Wilson
12. Stewart Kennedy
13. Greig, McKinnon and Baxter
14. Tom Forsyth
15. Egypt
16. Colin Stein
17. Eric Caldow
18. Davie Wilson
19. Northern Ireland and Wales
20. Sandy Jardine

13 *HAT-TRICK HEROES*

1. Robert Fleck
2. Ally McCoist
3. Raith Rovers
4. Gordon Smith
5. John Brown
6. Dave McPherson
7. Colin Stein
8. Dunfermline
9. Jocky Scott
10. Alex Ferguson
11. Four
12. Clydebank
13. Willie Johnston
14. Falkirk
15. Arbroath and Hibs
16. Mark Falco
17. Ralph Brand
18. Brian McClair
19. John MacDonald
20. Johnny Hubbard

14 DUNDEE, HAMILTON...

1. Kilmarnock
2. Forfar
3. Tynecastle
4. 1982
5. Robert Prytz
6. Easter Road
7. Davie Cooper
8. St Johnstone
9. Hearts
10. Airdrie
11. Brockville, Falkirk
12. Jim Stewart
13. 4–0 to Aberdeen
14. Third Lanark
15. Ayr United
16. Pittodrie
17. Inverness Caley
18. Valletta
19. John MacDonald
20. 4–0 in 1986–87

15 *JUST WILLIAM*

1. Sandy Jardine
2. Willie Henderson
3. West Bromwich
4. Northern Ireland
5. Willie Mathieson
6. Billy Davies
7. Billy Urquhart
8. Willie Thornton
9. Willie Findlay
10. New Zealand
11. Hearts
12. A 'Rest of Britain' select
13. Sheffield Wednesday
14. Musselburgh Athletic
15. Willie Paton
16. Partick Thistle
17. St Mirren
18. Willie Henderson
19. Hearts
20. Seven

16 BLUE IS THE COLOUR

1. Admiral
2. 1987
3. Red
4. The white 'V' collar
5. A crest (RFC)
6. All blue
7. Red-and-white diagonal halves
8. Monaco's
9. Davie Cooper
10. All white
11. Umbro
12. Pinstripes
13. Black with red tops
14. Blue-and-white striped shirts and white shorts
15. White 'wing' collar with blue and red trim
16. 1984
17. C. R. Smith
18. Red
19. Blue-and-white hooped shirts with white shorts
20. Derek Ferguson

17 THE MIDFIELD MEN

1. No.5
2. Neale Cooper
3. Celtic
4. Ian Redford
5. Johnny Hamilton
6. Airdrie
7. Derek Ferguson
8. Hamilton Accies
9. 1980
10. Two
11. Kenny Watson
12. Sammy Baird
13. Sweden
14. St Mirren
15. Shettleston Juniors
16. Cammy Fraser
17. 1985
18. Paris St Germain
19. Ian McColl
20. Dundee

18 EARLY BATHS

1. Hugh Burns and Craig Paterson
2. Willie Woodburn
3. Ankaragucu
4. Graham Roberts and Ian Durrant
5. It came after the final whistle
6. Tynecastle
7. Alex MacDonald
8. Frank McAvennie, Chris Woods and Terry Butcher
9. Jimmy Millar
10. Doug Bell and Jim Bett
11. Jim Leishman
12. Ally McCoist
13. Sandy Clark
14. Vojvodina
15. Dunfermline
16. Jimmy Nicholl
17. Gregor Stevens
18. John MacDonald
19. Dukla Prague
20. Calum Milne

19   *FINAL FLINGS*

1. Terry Butcher
2. Eric Black
3. Once
4. Sandy Jardine
5. 4–1 to Aberdeen
6. Neale Cooper
7. John MacDonald
8. Alex Miller
9. Jim Denny
10. Derek Johnstone
11. George McCluskey
12. Alfie Conn
13. Andy Lynch
14. Derek Johnstone
15. Graeme Souness and Davie Cooper
16. Joe Miller
17. 1973
18. Alex Ferguson
19. Colin Stein
20. Jim Craig

20 SLIM JIM

1. Raith Rovers
2. 1960
3. £17,500
4. The British Army
5. 1963
6. Twice
7. No.6
8. Pat Crerand
9. Jim McCalliog
10. Sunderland
11. Nottingham Forest
12. Gary Sobers
13. Davie White
14. Gornik
15. Vienna
16. 34
17. Denis Law
18. Four
19. The Black Watch
20. Stanley Matthews

21 GOING DUTCH

1. PSV Eindhoven
2. Sparta
3. The Super Cup
4. DWS Amsterdam
5. Enschede
6. The European Cup-Winners' Cup
7. Johan Cruyff
8. Alex MacDonald
9. Willy and Rene van der Kerkhof
10. Bobby Russell
11. Feyenoord
12. Jan Jongbloed
13. Ajax
14. Highbury
15. 'Total Football'
16. VfB Stuttgart
17. Ruud Gullit
18. Frank Stapleton
19. Frans Thijssen
20. Eindhoven

22 THEY SHALL NOT PASS

1. Stockholm, Sweden
2. Craig Paterson
3. Johansen and Provan
4. 1988
5. Dave Smith
6. Jimmy Nicholl and Scott Nisbet
7. George Brown
8. Mansfield Town
9. Graham Roberts
10. Tom Forsyth
11. Bobby Shearer
12. Hugh Burns
13. Colin Jackson
14. Richard Gough
15. Motherwell
16. Ally Dawson
17. Alloa
18. Sandy Jardine
19. Jock Shaw
20. Dundee United

23 WHO'S THE FELLOW IN THE BLACK?

1. Bob Valentine
2. Jim Duncan
3. David Syme
4. Arthur Ellis
5. He blew the final whistle seven minutes too early
6. *It's a Knockout*
7. Mike Delaney
8. Spanish
9. Jim Duncan
10. Jim Bett
11. Alex Poinet
12. Ian Foote
13. Bob Valentine
14. Kenny Hope
15. George Smith
16. Tom Wharton
17. 'Tiny'
18. Andrew Waddell
19. Bob Valentine
20. Brian McGinlay

24   1970s TREBLE CHANCES

1. Hearts
2. Tannadice
3. Alex MacDonald
4. Montrose
5. Sandy Jardine
6. Celtic
7. Derek Johnstone
8. Martin Henderson
9. Motherwell
10. John Greig
11. Aberdeen
12. Billy McNeill
13. Davie Cooper
14. Gordon Smith
15. 6–1
16. Forfar
17. Motherwell
18. Bobby Russell
19. Alex MacDonald
20. Derek Johnstone

25 *THE ENGLISH CONNECTION*

1. Seven
2. Spurs
3. Berwick
4. Burnley
5. Mel Sterland and Chris Morris
6. Neil Woods
7. Gary Stevens and Trevor Steven (Everton) and Mo Johnston (Watford)
8. Aston Villa
9. Nigel Spackman
10. Division Two
11. Norwich
12. 1985
13. The European Cup-Winners' Cup
14. Jimmy Phillips
15. Watford
16. Ray Wilkins
17. The Soviet Union
18. Atalanta
19. Spurs
20. Exeter City

26   *TOP SKOLARS*

1. Richard Gough
2. Three
3. Mark Walters
4. Dunfermline
5. Ian Durrant
6. Brian McClair
7. Graham Roberts
8. 3–3
9. Cooper, Durrant and Fleck
10. Jim Bett
11. Peter Nicholas
12. Ian Durrant
13. Iain Ferguson's
14. Craig Paterson
15. Ally McCoist
16. Ally Dawson
17. Dundee United
18. 1984
19. Richard Gough and Ally McCoist
20. Hibs

27 *BLUE MOVES*

1. FC Twente Enschede
2. Tynecastle
3. Rangers v St Johnstone, April 1991
4. Brian Reid
5. Hearts
6. St Mirren and Rangers (while he was still with Kiev)
7. Ipswich
8. Coventry City
9. Manchester United
10. John Brown
11. Morton
12. St Johnstone
13. Angus MacPherson
14. Millwall
15. Nigel Spackman
16. Adamslie Park
17. Gary Stevens
18. Dunfermline
19. Chris Vinnicombe
20. It was Graeme Souness!

28 GERS ON SONG

1. Barcelona and Real Madrid
2. 'A bunch of strangers'
3. 'We Are The Champions'
4. Ian Durrant
5. Kenny Dalglish
6. 'The Boys In Blue'
7. At the 1986 World Cup where Gary Stevens of Spurs was also in the England squad
8. 'Nice One Derek'
9. Andy Cameron
10. 'Who's That Team?'
11. Colin Stein
12. 'Championi'
13. Jim Bett
14. Sandy Jardine (and also Sandy Clark)
15. The East Enclosure
16. 'Glory Glory Glasgow Rangers'
17. 'We'll Support You Evermore'
18. Henry Smith
19. Derek Parlane
20. 'Say It With Pride'

29   *WE'RE GOING TO WIN THE LEAGUE*

1. More
2. Hibs
3. Colin Stein
4. Eleven
5. Ralph Brand
6. 18
7. Airdrie
8. Jock Shaw
9. Six
10. Bobby Shearer
11. Derek Parlane
12. Hearts
13. John Greig and Billy Ritchie
14. Jim Forrest
15. The Southern League
16. Hibs
17. 1976
18. Kilmarnock
19. Third
20. Aberdeen

30 *BARCELONA '72*

1. Rennes
2. He ordered a penalty shoot-out when Rangers should have been declared winners on the away goals rule
3. Willie Henderson
4. Colin Stein
5. Gomes
6. Ron McKinnon
7. Alex MacDonald
8. Paul Breitner
9. Sandy Jardine
10. Derek Parlane
11. John Greig
12. The Nou Camp
13. 20,000
14. 3–2
15. Colin Stein
16. Willie Johnston
17. Dave Smith
18. Colin Jackson
19. Derek Johnstone
20. Because of Scotland's Home International match with Wales on the same night

31 ON THE WING

1. Birmingham
2. Three
3. Left
4. Alan Morton
5. Willie Henderson and Willie Johnston
6. Davie Wilson
7. Quinton Young
8. Ted McMinn
9. Vancouver Whitecaps
10. Tommy McLean
11. Dundee United
12. Orjan Persson
13. Ian McCall
14. Queen of the South
15. South African
16. Kilmarnock
17. Hearts
18. Bobby McKean
19. Everton
20. Davie Wilson

32 BRING ON THE CELTIC

1. Terry Butcher
2. Bonny Ginzburg
3. Cammy Fraser
4. Mo Johnston
5. Ally McCoist
6. Kevin Drinkell
7. Ray Wilkins
8. Ian Andrews
9. 2–0 to Rangers
10. Ally Dawson and Davie Cooper
11. Richard Gough
12. Alex Miller
13. Anton Rogan
14. Mark Walters
15. Ian Durrant
16. 3–0
17. Jan Bartram
18. Hampden
19. Mo Johnston
20. Ally McCoist

33 D. J.

1. 16
2. 1978
3. Chelsea
4. John Greig
5. Wales
6. Central defender
7. Dundee United
8. Hearts
9. 1982
10. Partick Thistle
11. Switzerland
12. Dundee United
13. None
14. Cowdenbeath
15. No.5
16. Aberdeen
17. 14
18. Jim Craig
19. Six
20. 1986

34 IBROX STADIUM

1. The Copland Road Stand
2. Partick Thistle
3. Celtic
4. Alan Morton's
5. The Broomloan Road
6. The Centenary Stand
7. The USSR
8. Jim Watt
9. Edmiston Drive
10. The Scottish Junior Cup
11. Arsenal
12. The Govan Stand
13. 2–0 to Celtic
14. The Broomloan Road Stand
15. Hampden Park
16. Red, yellow, blue, orange and brown
17. 1981
18. The Edmiston Club
19. The Albion
20. The Broomloan Road

35 *WORLD CUP GERS*

1. Richard Gough, Mo Johnston and Ally McCoist
2. Cyprus and France
3. John McClelland
4. Four
5. Willie Henderson
6. Sandy Jardine
7. Bonny Ginzburg
8. Australia
9. Four
10. Willie Johnston
11. Limassol, Cyprus
12. Gary Stevens
13. Norway
14. Tom Forsyth
15. The match against Brazil
16. Robert Prytz
17. Czechoslovakia
18. Sammy Baird, in 1958
19. Colin Miller
20. One (v Costa Rica)

36 CHAMPIONIS – 1988–89

1. Kevin Drinkell and Mel Sterland
2. Pittodrie
3. Stuart Munro
4. Celtic (5–1)
5. Gary Stevens
6. Richard Gough
7. Hamilton Accies
8. Ian McCall
9. Motherwell
10. Richard Gough
11. Andy Gray
12. Ian Ferguson
13. Kevin Drinkell
14. Ally McCoist
15. Joe Miller
16. Aberdeen
17. Mike Galloway and Mark Walters
18. Dundee
19. Celtic
20. 3–0

37 *PASTA AND BOVRIL*

1. Turin
2. AC Milan
3. Fiorentina
4. It was played over two legs
5. Inter Milan
6. Benfica
7. Nine
8. Dino Zoff
9. Alex MacDonald and Gordon Smith
10. 4–3
11. San Siro
12. Liam Brady
13. Karl-Heinz Rummenigge
14. Alessandro Altobelli
15. John McClelland
16. Swedish
17. John Greig
18. Jim Forrest
19. Mauve
20. Gaetano Scirea

38   COOP

1. The League Cup in 1978
2. £100,000
3. Jack Steedman
4. Three
5. The Drybrough Cup
6. Dundee United in 1981
7. Peru
8. Jock Stein
9. 1986
10. Albert Tatlock of *Coronation Street*
11. Cardiff
12. No
13. It was a rare header
14. Aberdeen
15. Peter Grant
16. Wales
17. Yes
18. Robert Fleck
19. Bordeaux
20. The 1989 Scottish Cup Final

39   CUP OF WOE

1. Creaney and Wdowczyk
2. Berwick Rangers
3. Jock Wallace
4. Dunfermline
5. John Brown
6. Adrian Sprott
7. Dundee
8. Ian St John
9. 3–2
10. McCoist and Durrant
11. Derek Ferguson
12. Colin McAdam
13. Iain Ferguson
14. Ian Redford
15. 2–2
16. Hibs
17. Sammy Reid
18. Jim Forrest and George McLean
19. Aberdeen
20. John Brown (then with Dundee)

40 ANYWHERE, EVERYWHERE

1. Katowice
2. Terry Butcher
3. Moscow Dynamo
4. Valletta
5. 18–0
6. Fernando Gomes
7. 2–0 to Ilves Tampere
8. OGC Nice
9. Rapid Vienna
10. Prague
11. Falco and McCoist
12. Lillestrom
13. Mickey Walsh
14. Sandy Clark
15. St Etienne
16. Gough and McCoist
17. Marius Lacatus
18. Bohemians Dublin
19. Berne
20. Max Murray

41   ONCE A RANGER

1. John McClelland
2. Airdrie
3. Graham Roberts (Chelsea) and Bobby Williamson (Rotherham)
4. Darlington
5. John MacDonald
6. Kilmarnock
7. Jim Forrest
8. Davie Provan
9. Morton
10. Kenny Burns
11. Morton and Partick Thistle
12. Sandy Jardine
13. Don Mackay
14. Sheffield Wednesday
15. Billy Urquhart
16. Mel Sterland
17. Raith Rovers
18. Jan Bartram
19. Craig Brown
20. Hearts and Motherwell

42 *JUST A MO!*

1. Broomfield, Airdrie
2. Partick Thistle
3. Graham Taylor
4. 2–1 to Rangers
5. Wales
6. Spain
7. Two
8. Peter McCloy
9. Rangers
10. 2–0 to Everton
11. Aberdeen
12. Valletta
13. Frankie Vercauteren
14. Six
15. Sweden
16. Ibrox
17. Graham Mitchell
18. Bill McMurdo
19. No.10
20. 11

43 *LIFTING THE LEAGUE CUP*

1. Ian Redford
2. Aberdeen
3. Jim Bett
4. Hearts
5. Colin Jackson
6. Doug Rougvie
7. Derek Johnstone
8. Ally McLeod
9. Ron McKinnon
10. Alfie Conn
11. Davie Cooper
12. Raith Rovers
13. Stewart Kennedy
14. 3–2 to Rangers
15. Aberdeen
16. Harry Hood
17. Morton
18. Davie Cooper
19. Kilmarnock
20. Jim Casey

44   IN THE HOT SEAT

1. Jock Wallace
2. Willie Waddell
3. The Glasgow Cup, in May 1986
4. Scot Symon
5. Clyde
6. Seville
7. Davie White
8. Kilmarnock
9. Bobby Brown
10. Alex Ferguson and Jim McLean
11. Preston
12. William Wilton
13. Third Lanark
14. Dundee United
15. Alex Totten's
16. Tommy McLean
17. Scot Symon
18. Jock Wallace
19. Dundee
20. Ian McColl

45   1986–87 – THAT CHAMPIONSHIP SEASON

1. Hibs
2. Falkirk
3. Dundee United
4. Ian Redford
5. Nine
6. Hamilton Accies
7. Ally McCoist
8. Falkirk
9. Brian Irvine
10. St Mirren
11. Davie Cooper
12. Jim Leighton
13. Graham Roberts
14. Davie McPherson
15. Brian McClair
16. Ally McCoist
17. 25
18. Colin West
19. Ally McCoist
20. Most goals in a post-war season for Rangers

46 *GREIGY*

1. Edinburgh
2. 1961
3. Ian McMillan
4. The Soviet Union
5. 1964
6. Italy
7. 1966
8. 130
9. Left-back
10. He was unable to shave due to a cut chin
11. It was Rangers' 10,000th goal of all time
12. Ankaragucu
13. 1978
14. Five
15. 44
16. Billy Bremner
17. A Scotland select
18. 5–0 to Rangers
19. The MBE
20. Hearts

47 *CELEBRITY BEARS*

1. Marti Pellow
2. Ian Botham
3. Princess Alexandra
4. Bob Sutherland
5. Hughie Green
6. Rod Stewart
7. 2–0 to Rangers
8. Michael Foot
9. Eric Morley
10. Alexei Kosygin
11. Stephen Hendry
12. Mr Abie
13. Margaret Thatcher
14. Billy Rankin
15. Jim Callaghan
16. Steaua Bucharest
17. Sandy Jardine's
18. Winston Churchill
19. Lex McLean
20. Kenny Dalglish and Danny McGrain

48 OVER THE BORDER

1. Wolves
2. Arsenal
3. 8–4
4. Jimmy Greaves
5. They won it
6. Aston Villa
7. The quarter-finals
8. Billy Bremner
9. Peter Lorimer
10. Liverpool
11. 2–2
12. Andy Penman
13. Willie McFaul
14. Jim Scott and Jackie Sinclair
15. 1–1
16. Chesterfield
17. Phil Bonnyman
18. David Harvey
19. They watched it on closed-circuit TV at Ibrox
20. Jack Charlton and Alex Ferguson

49   THE NAME GAME

1. Ian McMillan
2. 'Bud'
3. Peter McCloy
4. David Meiklejohn
5. 'Razor'
6. Alex MacDonald
7. Ted McMinn
8. Don Kichenbrand
9. 'Cutty'
10. Ally Dawson
11. Davie MacKinnon
12. 'Bomber'
13. Alan Morton
14. George McLean
15. Jim Bett
16. 'Dody'
17. Tom Forsyth
18. Kevin Drinkell
19. 'Bucksy'
20. George Young – because he used to collect champagne corks

50 BOOKED!

1. Davie Cooper's
2. 1923
3. Archie MacPherson
4. John Greig
5. 1971
6. Willie Johnston
7. *No Half Measures*
8. *Playing for Rangers*
9. Bill Murray
10. *Both Sides of the Border*
11. Bob McPhail
12. Chick Young
13. *Even Stevens*
14. Derek Johnstone
15. *Growing with Glory*
16. Willie Waddell
17. *A Manager's Diary*
18. John Greig
19. *When the Going Gets Tough*
20. *Re-birth of the Blues*

51 OUT OF THE BLUE

1. John Greig
2. Sixth
3. Ally Dawson and John McClelland
4. Internacional Porto Alegre
5. Because the East German team had been refused visas to enter Britain
6. Aberdeen and Cologne
7. Gary Stevens
8. George Best
9. 1985–86
10. Gordon Smith
11. Alan Gilzean
12. John Greig
13. Motherwell
14. Sandy Jardine
15. They were unhappy that the width of the pitch had been reduced
16. 14–2
17. Jim Forrest and Alex Willoughby
18. The Tennents' Sixes
19. Thor Beck
20. Davie White